The Gardening
CROSSWORD BOOK

Michael Curl

igloo

The Gardening
CROSSWORD BOOK

Michael Curl

Answers are on pages 204–224.

First Garden

The grid at position 22 across reads: **THE GARDEN OF EDEN**

Let's start with a garden that's truly original. Time to dig in!

Across

7 Inexpensive (5)
9 South Pole region (9)
11 Left out (7)
12 Cow's sound (3)
13 Domestic fuel (3)
15 Muhammad ___, heavyweight boxing champion (3)
16 Great river of Egypt (4)
18 Heavenly bodies (5)
22 FIRST GARDEN (3,6,2,4)
25 Impertinence (5)
28 Notorious Roman fiddler (4)
29 Climbing vegetable plant bearing pods (3)
31 Scarlet (3)
33 Afternoon meal (3)
34 One name (anagram) – colourful hardy perennial (7)
36 Common yellow weed (9)
37 Secret agents (5)

Down

1 Reflected sound (4)
2 The sign of the twins (6)
3 Magician's rod (4)
4 Archer's missiles (6)
5 Male deer (4)
6 Frozen refreshments (4)
8 A nut pie (anagram) – spring bedding plant (7)
10 Domesticated (4)
14 Atmosphere (3)
15 Room at the Top? (5)
17 Traditional children's board game (4)
19 Assist (3)
20 Father Christmas (5)
21 Leg joint (4)
23 Female sheep (3)
24 Blooms (7)
26 Gardening tool (3)
27 Young cat (6)
29 Gain (6)
30 Bathroom powder (4)
31 Dress (4)
32 Fruit from a palm tree (4)
34 European mountain range (4)
35 Not difficult (4)

Celebrity Gardener

6

When the crossword is completed, the shaded squares will spell out the name of a famous gardener.

Across

1 Broadcasting medium (5)
4 Arabian Nights hero (3,4)
8 Disperse (7)
9 Cheap wine of inferior quality (5)
10 Regretted (4)
11 Vegetable that is an emblem of Wales (4)
13 Young goat (3)
15 Title given to a nun (6)
17 Spasmodic muscle contraction (6)
20 20 hundredweight (3)
21 Ollie's partner (4)
22 Agricultural establishment (4)
25 Seventh sign of the Zodiac (5)
28 Let go (7)
29 Not deep (7)
30 Does as one is told (5)

Down

1 Holiday destinations (7)
2 Male duck (5)
3 Solemn vow (4)
4 Concurred (6)
5 Mischievous child (3)
6 Fuss (3)
7 Enquired (5)
12 New Zealand bird – or fruit (4)
13 Equipment (3)
14 Insects in a hive (4)
16 Male child (3)
18 Picnic baskets (7)
19 Famous public school (6)
20 Cash registers (5)
23 Not asleep (5)
24 As well (4)
26 Snake that squeezes its prey (3)
27 Be unwell (3)

Highly Popular

When the crossword is completed, the shaded squares will spell out a flower that's highly popular!

Across

1 Bike rider (7)
5 Speedy (4)
7 Elton John's instrument (5)
8 Colour of kingcups (6)
10 Way out (4)
11 Abandoned, deserted (8)
13 Manservant (6)
14 Russia's capital (6)
17 Climbing plant with fragrant pastel-coloured flowers (5,3)
19 Paving slab – or iris (4)
22 Graduate's qualification (6)
23 Trip the light fantastic (5)
24 Buds on a potato tuber (4)
25 Increased threefold (7)

Down

1 Wood, thicket (5)
2 Haricot (anagram) – old war vehicle (7)
3 Magnetic metal (4)
4 Gordon ___, one of the presenters of the TV show "The Curious Gardener" (6)
5 Punctuation mark (4,4)
6 Night-scented ___, fragrant hardy annual (5)
9 Falling flakes (4)
12 False teeth (8)
13 Gaffer (4)
15 Army rank (7)
16 Say or do again (6)
18 Foe (5)
20 Avarice (5)
21 Brink (4)

Flower Show

When the crossword is completed, the shaded squares will spell out the venue for a famous flower show.

Across

1   "Parsley, sage, rosemary and ___" (5)
4   Royal Engineers (7)
8   Scrutinise (7)
9   Potatoes – or digging tools (5)
10 The two of them (4)
11 Mark left by a wound (4)
13 Writing implement (3)
15 Act as a stimulant (6)
17 Chess piece (6)
20 Perform a role (3)
21 Silence (4)
22 Pitcher (4)
25 Voracious fish (5)
28 Give or bring back (7)
29 Lurch (7)
30 Bar of bullion (5)

Down

1   Quiver (7)
2   Organism causing fermentation (5)
3   One of the Great Lakes (4)
4   Preliminary drawing (6)
5   Fathers (3)
6   Flightless Australian bird (3)
7   Black-eyed ___ (thunbergia) (5)
12 Skating arena (4)
13 Washing line pin (3)
14 Skin irritation (4)
16 Incision (3)
18 Rushing stream (7)
19 Extortionate money-lender (6)
20 Donkeys (5)
23 Incorrect (5)
24 Sparkling Italian wine (4)
26 ___ Gardner, film star (3)
27 Small barrel (3)

Houseplant

When the crossword is completed, the shaded squares will spell out the name of a popular houseplant.

Across

1 West Indian song, usually topical (7)
5 Be afraid (4)
7 Slight colouring (5)
8 Very dirty (6)
10 Very warm (3)
11 Unit of land measurement (4)
12 The Orient (4)
14 Outcome (6)
15 Enclosed – or fought with swords (6)
18 Nobleman (4)
20 Capital of Peru (4)
21 Fly catcher? (3)
24 Send into exile (6)
25 Layabout (5)
26 Leave out (4)
27 Church spire (7)

Down

1 Capture (5)
2 Syrupy medicine (7)
3 Animal that preys on others (8)
4 University city (6)
5 Autumn (4)
6 Greenfly (5)
9 Ali ___, gardening writer and TV presenter (4)
13 Member of the family (8)
14 Not new (4)
16 Spring flower (Primula veris) (7)
17 Illuminations (6)
19 Domain (5)
22 Canal boat (5)
23 Present (4)

Celebrity Gardener

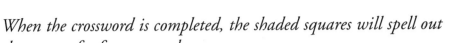

When the crossword is completed, the shaded squares will spell out the name of a famous gardener.

Across

1	Emblem of royalty (7)
5	Fraction of a foot (4)
7	Become void (5)
8	Recess (6)
10	Expensive (4)
11	Cul-de-sacs (4,4)
13	Start of the working week usually (6)
14	Hostility (6)
17	Sane (8)
19	It turns litmus red (4)
22	Insect with large rear pincers (6)
23	Hurry (5)
24	Rip (4)
25	Comments (7)

Down

1	Lettuce, cucumber, radishes, etc. (5)
2	Elucidate (7)
3	Fastened (4)
4	Rubbed out (6)
5	Event (8)
6	Assembly of witches (5)
9	Children's guessing game (1-3)
12	Fighting ship (3-2-3)
13	Female horse (4)
15	Narrow-edged tooth (7)
16	Animal at home in a sett (6)
18	Rachel de ___, Gardeners' World presenter (5)
20	Clothe (5)
21	Pal (4)

Favourite Flower

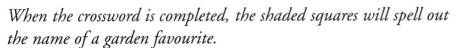

When the crossword is completed, the shaded squares will spell out
the name of a garden favourite.

Across

1 Green salad plant (7)
5 Containers for plants (4)
7 Fairytale monster (5)
8 Look at (3)
9 Young fellow (3)
11 Hogs (4)
12 Period of unusually hot
    weather (4,4)
14 Garb (6)
15 Assisted (6)
18 Go far ahead of (8)
20 Labyrinth (4)
23 Objective (3)
24 Colour of rose-hips (3)
25 Incompetent (5)
26 _____ salad, another name for
    lamb's lettuce (4)
27 Arum lip (anagram) – spring
    bedding plant (7)

Down

1 Illuminated (3,2)
2 Idea (7)
3 Far from fair (4)
4 Football or cricket team (6)
5 Pacts (8)
6 Wood for model makers (5)
10 Great fear (5)
13 Brothers (8)
14 Fragrance (5)
16 High level ground (7)
17 Bound (4,2)
19 Speed, in music (5)
21 Additional (5)
22 Audio equipment (2-2)

Herbaceous Border

When the crossword is completed, the shaded squares will spell out a traditional plant for the herbaceous border.

Across

1	Vagrant (5)
4	Evaluate (6)
7	Tiny (3)
8	Toy bear (5)
9	Towards the stern (3)
11	Floral emblem of Ireland (8)
13	Cease (4)
15	Detective (6)
16	Almost (6)
19	Floral emblem of England (4)
21	Floral emblem of Wales (8)
24	Light brown (3)
25	Margins (5)
27	Industrious insect (3)
28	Core (6)
29	Go in (5)

Down

1	Urban areas (5)
2	Mean, medium (7)
3	Favourite (3)
4	Junkie (6)
5	"Over the Sea to ___" (4)
6	Begin (5)
10	Squiffy (5)
12	Long-tailed rodents (4)
14	Unable to hear (4)
15	Fish to catch a mackerel? (5)
17	Glowing (7)
18	Hang loosely (6)
20	Burn slightly (5)
22	Afterwards (5)
23	Canterbury's county (4)
26	Observe (3)

Novel

When the crossword is completed, the shaded squares will spell out the title of a classic novel with a "flowery" theme.

Across

1 Shakespeare's Scottish play (7)
5 Garden building (4)
7 Red-breasted bird (5)
8 Move head in agreement (3)
9 At present (3)
11 Yellow part of an egg (4)
12 Pears lie (anagram) – trellis on which a shrub or fruit tree is trained to grow flat (8)
15 Most uncommon (6)
16 Largest of the Channel Islands (6)
19 Accentuated (8)
21 Pulled or drawn tight (4)
24 Droop (3)
25 Everything (3)
26 Heather genus (5)
27 In this place (4)
28 Popeye's favourite vegetable (7)

Down

1 Joyous (5)
2 Mender of shoes (7)
3 Sicilian volcano (4)
4 Free from guile (6)
5 Unhappy (3)
6 Tedium (5)
10 Concern (5)
13 High cards (4)
14 Makes a request (4)
15 Floribundas, hybrid teas, etc. (5)
17 Endurance, staying power (7)
18 ___ perennis (daisy) (6)
20 Scoundrel (5)
22 Rubbish (5)
23 Suburban house (4)
25 Chopping tool (3)

Herb Garden

22

We provide a selection of herbs for your garden. All you have to do is plant them out in the correct positions!

ARTEMISIA	MARJORAM
BASIL	MILFOIL
BERGAMOT	MINT
BETONY	PARSLEY
BURDOCK	PURSLANE
CHAMOMILE	ROCKET
CHIVES	SORREL
COMFREY	THYME
CORIANDER	VALERIAN
FENNEL	

What's on TV?

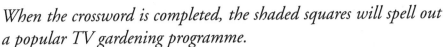

*When the crossword is completed, the shaded squares will spell out
a popular TV gardening programme.*

Across

1   Garbage (7)
5   Garment in ancient Rome (4)
7   Web-footed birds (5)
8   Pleasing to many (7)
10 One of the four evangelists (4)
11 Period before Easter (4)
13 Be seated (3)
15 Child who has lost both parents (6)
16 Commands (6)
19 Drag (3)
21 At that time (4)
22 A rolling stone gathers no ___ (4)
25 Tell a story (7)
27 Combine (5)
28 Buddy (4)
29 Coach (7)

Down

1   Royal, majestic (5)
2   Separate (5,2)
3   "Beware the __ of March" (4)
4   Occur (6)
5   Spinning toy (3)
6   Fierce winds (5)
9   Property tax (5)
12 Rotate (4)
14 Stop (4)
15 Frequently (5)
17 Feeling, sentiment (7)
18 Flaw (6)
20 Value (5)
23 Asparagus shoot (5)
24 Canned fish (4)
26 Limb (3)

Spring Bedding

¹		²		³		⁴		⁵		⁶		⁷

When the crossword is completed, the shaded squares will spell out the name of a spring bedding plant.

Across

1 Difficult question (5)
4 Common garden bird (7)
8 Big ape (7)
9 Red-suited Christmas visitor (5)
10 Location (4)
11 Something owed (4)
13 Purchase (3)
15 Holy (6)
17 Capital of Cuba (6)
20 Long-tailed rodent (3)
21 Bye-bye (2-2)
22 Cream of the crop (4)
25 Treasure container? (5)
28 Not artificial (7)
29 Intention (7)
30 Inferior (5)

Down

1 Mythical winged horse (7)
2 Swagger (5)
3 Swiss ___ (cylindrical cake) (4)
4 Weighing machine (6)
5 Classifieds (3)
6 Compete in a race (3)
7 Fatigued (5)
12 Title of Russian emperors (4)
13 Sheep's cry (3)
14 "The garden of England" (4)
16 Incision (3)
18 Set bail (anagram) – herbaceous plant (7)
19 Immediately (2,4)
20 Go over it again (5)
23 Mistake (5)
24 Put away for storage (4)
26 Always (in poetry) (3)
27 A couple (3)

Hybrid Tea

*When the crossword is completed, the shaded squares will spell out
the name of a classic hybrid tea rose.*

Across

1   Distended (7)
5   Make up one's mind (6)
8   Hawaiian greeting (5)
9   Hat-maker (8)
11 Irritated (7)
13 Farewell (7)
15 Miniature variety (5)
17 Large town (4)
19 Children's card game (4)
21 Denuded of leaves (4)
22 Dish of food cooked in water or
    stock (4)
25 Painting stand (5)
27 Supplement to a will (7)
29 Excel (7)
31 Severe headache (8)
33 Russian liquor (5)
34 Going by air (6)
35 See main (anagram) – annual
    flower (7)

Down

1   Discoloured (7)
2   Fresh bracing air (5)
3   Meadow (3)
4   Wandering from place to place (7)
5   Delectation (7)
6   One of the Marx Brothers (5)
7   Female rabbit (3)
10 Shed tears (4)
12 Dig up a crop such as potatoes (4)
14 Extra payment (5)
16 Pungent (5)
18 Frozen water (3)
20 Twelvemonth (4)
21 Rear (4)
23 Working the land (7)
24 Cowboy story (7)
26 Milan opera house (2,5)
28 Welsh breed of dog (5)
30 S. American mountain range (5)
32 Ailing (3)
33 ___ and vigour (3)

Fragrance

30

When the crossword is completed, the shaded squares will spell out the name of a flower with fragrant leaves.

Across

1   Prime minister (7)
5   Universe – or summer-flowering annual (6)
8   Din (5)
9   NCO (8)
11   Whole number (7)
13   Autumn month (7)
15   Be superior (5)
17   Female sheep (4)
19   Donate (4)
21   Rove (4)
22   The maple genus of trees (4)
25   Carmen, for example (5)
27   Excuse (7)
29   Scoundrel (7)
31   Confidently optimistic and cheerful (8)
33   Papa (5)
34   Ice-cream cone (6)
35   Highly regarded (7)

Down

1   Thoughtful (7)
2   Decree (5)
3   Frozen sweet (3)
4   Keep back (7)
5   Rust (7)
6   Worn out (5)
7   Possess (3)
10   Genuine (4)
12   Fierce wind (4)
14   Newly married woman (5)
16   Stop (5)
18   Misery (3)
20   Rock and ____ (4)
21   Fully matured and ready to be eaten (4)
23   Perennial herb (Nepeta cataria) (7)
24   Mediterranean holiday area (7)
26   Vexed (7)
28   Incite (3,2)
30   Venomous snake (5)
32   "Much ____ About Nothing" (3)
33   Faint (3)

Spring

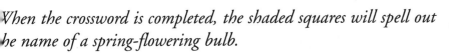

When the crossword is completed, the shaded squares will spell out the name of a spring-flowering bulb.

Across

- Yearned (6)
- Petty quarrel (4)
- Twenty-four hours (3)
- 0 Aristocratic (5)
- 1 Fifth sign of the zodiac (3)
- 2 Sum (5)
- 3 Concealed ditch used in landscape gardening (2-2)
- 5 One of the Great Lakes (8)
- 9 Counterfeit (7)
- 20 Medical treatment (7)
- 22 Capital of Burma (7)
- 24 Make a wry face (7)
- 25 Unseemly (8)
- 26 Feudal worker (4)
- 30 Public disturbances (5)
- 32 Before, poetically (3)
- 33 Large group of fish (5)
- 35 Positive answer (3)
- 36 Fledgling's home (4)
- 37 Military pageant (6)

Down

- 1 Midday meal (5)
- 2 Pen-point (3)
- 3 Looked at (4)
- 5 Defend (7)
- 6 Small bird (3)
- 7 Discourage (5)
- 8 Christmas (4)
- 9 Overcast (6)
- 14 Long-legged long-necked wading bird (5)
- 16 Candytuft (6)
- 17 On the far side (6)
- 18 Write, using a keyboard (4)
- 19 Tool with prongs (4)
- 21 Astound (5)
- 23 US coins (7)
- 24 Male goose (6)
- 25 Jeremy ___ (film star) (5)
- 27 Large book size (5)
- 28 Helen of ___ (4)
- 29 One of the continents (4)
- 31 Centre of a solar system (3)
- 34 Not indoors (3)

Heavenly Light

*When the crossword is completed, the shaded squares will spell out
the name of a "heavenly light bulb"!*

Across

1 Item of playground equipment (5)
4 Flying mammals (4)
7 Mischievous sprite (3)
10 Book of maps (5)
12 Produce an egg (3)
13 Long, pine (5)
14 Thomas, familiarly (3)
15 Juliet's lover (5)
17 Operations (abbreviated) (3)
18 Deadly (5)
19 Sumptuous meal (7)
21 Mixed (7)
23 Mapped (7)
25 Everywhere (3,4)
27 Below (5)
29 Contend in rivalry (3)
30 Gesture of indifference (5)
32 Almond, for example (3)
33 ___ Minogue (singer) (5)
35 Slender stick (3)
36 Different (5)
39 Before (in poetry) (3)
40 In those days (4)
41 Troublesome little insect (5)

Down

1 The Adriatic, for example (3)
2 Unwell (3)
3 Zest, relish (5)
5 Lay sums (anagram) – popular
  bedding plant (7)
6 Firmament (3)
7 Precise (5)
8 Caressed (7)
9 Nearly (6)
11 A pair (3)
15 Steal from (3)
16 Food from heaven (5)
18 Last (5)
20 Out-and-out (5)
22 Bile-secreting organ (5)
23 Quiet laugh (7)
24 Varied (7)
25 List of things to be done (6)
26 Outfit (3)
28 Dig (5)
30 Tempest (5)
31 Utilise (3)
34 Have a meal (3)
37 Concealed (3)
38 Fish eggs (3)

Damp

When the crossword is completed, the shaded squares will spell out the name of a plant suitable for damp areas.

Across

1 Tower on a mosque (7)
5 Maiden in distress? (6)
8 Use a divining-rod (5)
9 Use badly (3-5)
11 Set aside for future use (7)
13 Afternoon show (7)
15 Hairdresser's establishment (5)
17 June 6th, 1944 (1-3)
19 Spoken (4)
21 Small child (4)
22 Merriment (4)
25 One who shows people to their seats (5)
27 Give authority to (7)
29 Formal discussions (7)
31 One of Shakespeare's tragedies (4,4)
33 Keen (5)
34 Half-tamed variety of polecat (6)
35 Correctness of behaviour (7)

Down

1 Insanity (7)
2 More recent (5)
3 Bitter-tasting herb (3)
4 Deceived (7)
5 Predicament (7)
6 Deserve (5)
7 Historical period (3)
10 Back part of the foot (4)
12 Green Gables girl (4)
14 Compass point (5)
16 Abatement, alleviation (3-2)
18 Expire (3)
20 Without feeling (4)
21 Submissive (4)
23 Of greatest size (7)
24 Borne (7)
26 Platform for public speaking (7)
28 Bet (5)
30 Large striped cat (5)
32 Nickname of US president Eisenhower (3)
33 And so forth (abbr.) (3)

Popular Shrub

When the crossword is completed, the shaded squares will spell out the name of a popular shrub.

Across

1	Arise (3,2)
4	Crustacean – or type of apple (4)
7	Nervous twitch (3)
10	Fashion (5)
12	Lubricant (3)
13	Sleeper's vision (5)
14	Chump (3)
15	Bait, rag (5)
17	Half a dozen (3)
18	Russian liquor (5)
19	Bounce back (7)
21	Determined (7)
23	Caretaker (7)
25	Cut of beef (7)
27	Artificial gems (5)
29	Scheduled to arrive (3)
30	Reimburse (5)
32	Look at (3)
33	Hit hard (5)
35	Snake (3)
36	Footwear (5)
39	Balderdash (3)
40	A long time (4)
41	The devil (5)

Down

1	Cooking fuel (3)
2	Plaything (3)
3	Fold in fabric (5)
5	At ease (7)
6	Naughty (3)
7	Trample (5)
8	Order (7)
9	Thrown carelessly (6)
11	Contents of a cuppa? (3)
15	Old salt (3)
16	Not rural (5)
18	Parish clergyman (5)
20	Loosen (5)
22	Wilt (5)
23	Largest of the planets (7)
24	Bureaucratic procedure (3,4)
25	Drowsy (6)
26	No (3)
28	Crouch (5)
30	Takes a break (5)
31	Impress deeply (3)
34	Plant producing pods with edible seeds (3)
37	Frequently (3)
38	Male child (3)

Flowering Houseplant

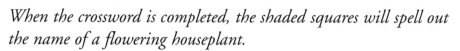

*When the crossword is completed, the shaded squares will spell out
the name of a flowering houseplant.*

Across

1 Backless couch (5)
4 Pavement edge (4)
7 Plant juice (3)
10 Device for measuring spirits in a pub (5)
12 Pen-point (3)
13 Larceny (5)
14 Very warm (3)
15 Film (5)
17 Epoch (3)
18 Duffer (5)
19 British soldier, formerly (7)
21 Graceful, refined (7)
23 Weightier (7)
25 Capable of being seen (7)
27 Workers' organisation (5)
29 Attempt (3)
30 Building offering accommodation (5)
32 Had some food (3)
33 High ground (5)
35 Floor covering (3)
36 Bare (5)
39 Coniferous tree (3)
40 Broad (4)
41 Vacant (5)

Down

1 Pair of performers (3)
2 Animal doctor (3)
3 Shallow recess (5)
5 Hug (7)
6 Portion (3)
7 Gloss (5)
8 Doctor's client (7)
9 Concentrating (6)
11 In favour (3)
15 Impair (3)
16 Russian liquor (5)
18 Sediment (5)
20 Edible bulb (5)
22 Head of a community of monks (5)
23 Proud (7)
24 Went to bed (7)
25 Sea journey (6)
26 Long slippery fish (3)
28 Relative by marriage (2-3)
30 From this place (5)
31 Lamb's mother (3)
34 Observed (3)
37 Sleep (3)
38 In need of watering (3)

Vegetable Garden

It's time for some work in the vegetable garden. There are twenty-one types of vegetable for you to transplant!

BEAN	KALE
BEETROOT	LEEK
BROCCOLI	LETTUCE
CABBAGE	ONION
CAPSICUM	PARSNIP
CARROT	SHALLOT
CELERIAC	SQUASH
CELERY	SWEDE
CHICORY	TOMATO
COURGETTE	TURNIP
ENDIVE	

Tree

When the crossword is completed, the shaded squares will spell out the name of a small deciduous tree.

Across

1 County in East Anglia (7)
5 Talon (4)
10 Pulled along with a rope (5)
11 Small variety of orange (9)
12 Under (7)
14 One of Shakespeare's plays (7)
16 Discolour (5)
18 Tennyson, for example (4)
20 Untruthful person (4)
23 Good fortune (4)
25 ___ Guinness, knighted actor (4)
28 Bottomless gulf (5)
30 Entering (5,2)
33 Diminished (7)
35 Change into another shape (9)
36 Disabled (5)
38 Statue in Piccadilly Circus (4)
39 Dictionary (7)

Down

1 Head, slangily (3)
2 Mountain ash (5)
3 Peculiar (3)
4 Sauce (7)
6 Blood-sucking worm (5)
7 Revolve rapidly (5)
8 Nap (6)
9 Consume (6)
12 Public transport vehicle (3)
13 Female relative (4)
15 Long slippery fish (3)
17 Joan of ___, French heroine (3)
19 A single (3)
21 Climbing plant (3)
22 Difficult (4)
23 Illuminations (6)
24 Family (3)
26 ___ pride (perennial saxifrage) (6)
27 Chewy sweet (7)
29 Doleful (3)
31 Picture (5)
32 Vigorous and enthusiastic enjoyment (5)
34 Humorous (5)
36 Slack (3)
37 Monty ___, Gardeners' World presenter (3)

Apple

*When the crossword is completed, the shaded squares will spell out
the name of a variety of apple.*

Across

1 Mushrooms and toadstools (5)
4 Brewer's cart (4)
6 Female servant (4)
9 Small pointed tool (3)
10 Alter with a view to improvement (5)
11 Worth (5)
12 Artificial waterway (5)
14 Idle bee (5)
15 Armed conflict (3)
17 Be present (6)
20 Word with the same meaning (7)
23 Pariah (7)
25 Edible nut (6)
28 That woman (3)
30 Creature that eats bamboo shoots (5)
31 Gumption (5)
33 Very sweet confection (5)
34 River of Paris (5)
35 Burnt remains (3)
36 Scottish dance (4)
37 Suspend (4)
38 Desiccated (5)

Down

1 Complete failure (6)
2 Synthetic fabric (5)
3 Perfectly suited (5)
4 Greatly feared (7)
5 Laborious, gruelling (7)
7 Acknowledge, concede (5)
8 Colouring substance (3)
11 Country of south-east Asia (7)
13 Fitting (3)
16 Slope (4)
18 Small child (3)
19 Instance (7)
21 Mother Teresa, for example (3)
22 The two of them (4)
24 North African country (7)
25 Astounding (7)
26 Type of poem (3)
27 Systematic procedure (6)
29 Crest (5)
31 Riding horse (5)
32 Provider of canteens for the armed services (5)
33 In favour (3)

Annual

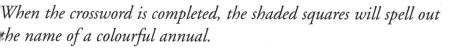

When the crossword is completed, the shaded squares will spell out the name of a colourful annual.

Across

1 Plotted (7)
5 Petty quarrel (4)
10 Something of value (5)
11 Uninterrupted (9)
12 Ate lavishly (7)
14 Can containing a spray (7)
15 Awaken (5)
17 Animal with antlers (4)
19 Slender (4)
22 Observed (4)
23 A long time (4)
26 Loft (5)
28 Tense, repressed (7)
31 Retort (7)
33 Capable (9)
34 ___ Thrower, former TV gardening expert (5)
36 Profound (4)
37 Get a move on (5,2)

Down

1 The Aegean, for example (3)
2 Plantain lily (5)
3 Floor covering (3)
4 Made up one's mind (7)
6 Previous (5)
7 Tuft of flowers or fruit at the top of the main stem (5)
8 Crazy (6)
9 Winding downhill ski race (6)
12 Evergreen tree (3)
13 Arduous journey (4)
16 Employ (3)
18 Look at (3)
20 Ignited (3)
21 Pond fish (4)
22 Origin (6)
24 Accumulate (6)
25 Minor abrasion (7)
27 Rod used in playing billiards (3)
29 Faint-hearted (5)
30 Web-footed birds (5)
32 Word of apology (5)
34 Standard score for golfers (3)
35 Shrill bark (3)

Celebrity Gardener

When the crossword is completed, the shaded squares will spell out the name of a celebrity gardener.

Across

1 Novice (7)
5 Cab (4)
10 Appear unexpectedly (3,2)
11 Dianthus (9)
12 Appalling (7)
14 Caretaker (7)
15 Credit or prestige (5)
17 Go down (4)
19 A large number (4)
22 Castro's land (4)
23 Makes enquiries (4)
26 Urge forward (5)
28 Dig up (7)
31 Huge (7)
33 Soon crept (anagram) – rockery plant (9)
34 Devastation (5)
36 Gaelic (4)
37 Climbing rose (7)

Down

1 Insolence (3)
2 Put to use (5)
3 Short sleep (3)
4 Remembers (7)
6 Once more (5)
7 Ninny (5)
8 Citizen of Troy (6)
9 Vigour (6)
12 Noah's vessel (3)
13 Bryophyte (4)
16 Gentle touch or wipe (3)
18 Annoy (3)
20 Unit of electric current (3)
21 Movie (4)
22 Sea trip (6)
24 Vast desert of North Africa (6)
25 Captain (7)
27 Stay flat (3)
29 Run away to be married (5)
30 Plants providing thatching material (5)
32 Umbilicus – or type of orange (5)
34 Border (3)
35 Automobile (3)

Clean Hands

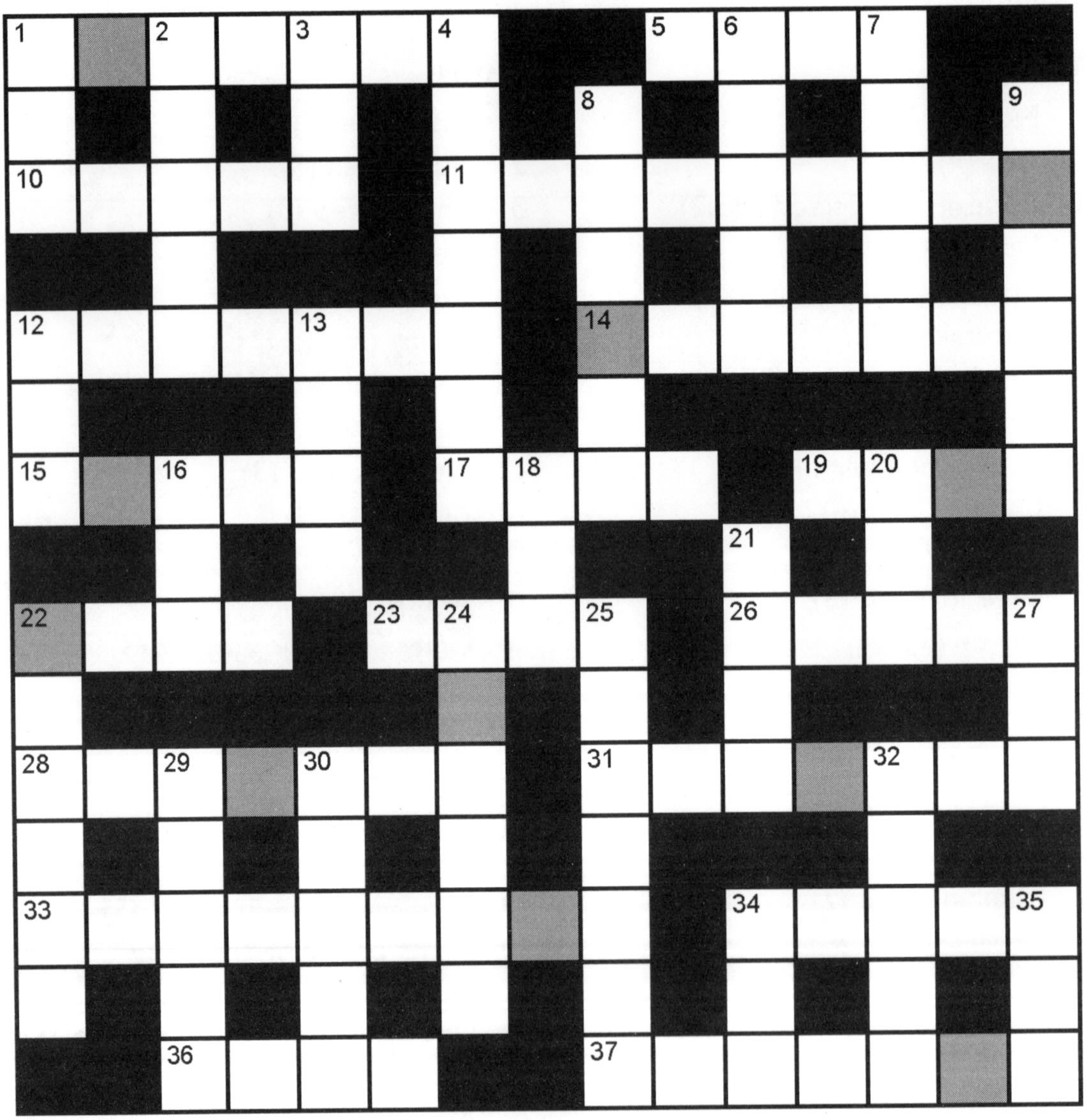

When the crossword is completed, the shaded squares will spell out a form of gardening for those who don't like getting their hands dirty!

Across

1 Excluded (4,3)
5 Young cow (4)
10 Quoted (5)
11 Pond plant (5,4)
12 Idealist, visionary (7)
14 Marine mammal (7)
15 Comical (5)
17 Catch sight of (4)
19 Slow pace of running (4)
22 Breakwater (4)
23 Stuart queen (4)
26 Stand-offish (5)
28 Small ornament or piece of jewellery (7)
31 Open grassland in the USA (7)
33 In an undertone (5,4)
34 Insect larvae (5)
36 Depend (4)
37 Most sorrowful (7)

Down

1 Intentionally so written (used after a printed word or phrase) (3)
2 Loosen (5)
3 Strange (3)
4 In the direction of (7)
6 Spring month (5)
7 Belief (5)
8 Artist's workroom (6)
9 Young swan (6)
12 Father (3)
13 Stubborn animal (4)
16 Material for smelting (3)
18 Play on words (3)
20 Brazilian city (3)
21 Cheerio (2-2)
22 Fertiliser (6)
24 Idea (6)
25 Female ruler (7)
27 Payment (3)
29 Bury (5)
30 Hillock (5)
32 Itinerary (5)
34 Deity (3)
35 Take a seat (3)

Sweet Pea

When the crossword is completed, the shaded squares will spell out the name of a variety of sweet pea.

Across

1   Appease, pacify (7)
5   Musical note (5)
9   Parts of plants below ground (5)
10 Wrecked (9)
11 Defamation (7)
13 Liverpool racecourse (7)
15 Burdened (5)
17 Compass bearing (4)
19 Labour (4)
21 Young lions, etc. (4)
22 Eating plan (4)
25 Plantain lily (5)
27 Lured (7)
29 Eight-sided figure (7)
31 Increase (9)
33 Biblical leader (5)
34 Available for rent (2,3)
35 Clergyman's house (7)

Down

1   Sunshade (7)
2   Fragrance (5)
3   Commercials (3)
4   Back (7)
5   Idiot (5)
6   No (3)
7   Wednesday or thereabouts (7)
8   Prose compositions (6)
12 Have a meal (4)
14 Crows (5)
16 First appearance (5)
18 Chopper (3)
20 Chinwag (4)
21 Pharmacist (7)
23 In fact, truly (6)
24 Pig's foot (7)
26 General pardon (7)
28 Play unfairly (5)
30 Zest (5)
32 A pass in a mountain-range (3)
33 Raincoat (3)

Spring Flower

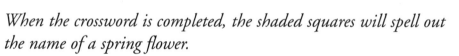

When the crossword is completed, the shaded squares will spell out
the name of a spring flower.

Across

1 Beautiful girl (5)
4 Liberate (3,4)
9 Herb with finely divided aromatic foliage (9)
10 Inflexible (5)
11 Zodiac sign (3)
12 Settee (4)
14 Small brook (4)
15 Meat (4)
19 "___ Coins in the Fountain" (5)
20 Marigold (9)
23 Beekeepers (9)
24 Brief letters (5)
25 Old English drink made with fermented honey (4)
27 Festival (4)
28 Egg on (4)
31 ___ Peron (Argentinian leader) (3)
33 Animal compartment (5)
35 Wretched (9)
37 Disrobe (7)
38 Drab (5)

Down

1 Defensive players (5)
2 Meadow (3)
3 Famous public school (4)
4 Odour (5)
5 Pulsate (5)
6 Floor covering (3)
7 Swirl of water (4)
8 Flowering shrub also known as mallow (8)
13 Stealthy (7)
16 Line round the middle of the earth (7)
17 Rend (4)
18 Snoozes (4)
19 Snare (4)
21 Languid, apathetic (8)
22 Not any (4)
26 Dig (5)
27 Pastimes (5)
29 Sad or reflective poem (5)
30 Son of Isaac (4)
32 Jab, nudge (4)
34 Append (3)
36 Arch (3)

Famous Garden

When the crossword is completed, the shaded squares will spell out the name of a famous garden.

Across

1 Bishop's district (7)
5 Unlucky accident (6)
8 Grass-like plant with a triangular stem (5)
9 Example (8)
11 Shorten (7)
13 Stuck (7)
15 Smears (5)
17 Fastened (4)
19 Fury (4)
21 Greet enthusiastically (4)
22 Lads (4)
25 Aromatic herb (5)
27 Lengthiest (7)
29 Conciliate (7)
31 Defer (8)
33 Trembling poplar (5)
34 Observation, comment (6)
35 Principled (7)

Down

1 Throw away (7)
2 More mature (5)
3 Apple eater in Eden (3)
4 Obvious (7)
5 Error (7)
6 Secret store (5)
7 Curve (3)
10 Tool used to cut and shape wood (4)
12 Twilight (4)
14 Poised for action (5)
16 Combination (5)
18 Frozen (3)
20 Halt (4)
21 One of two equal parts (4)
23 Prospect (7)
24 Breed of cat (7)
26 Perpetual (7)
28 Surplus (5)
30 Savoury jelly (5)
32 Be indebted (3)
33 Tree with keys (3)

Runner Bean

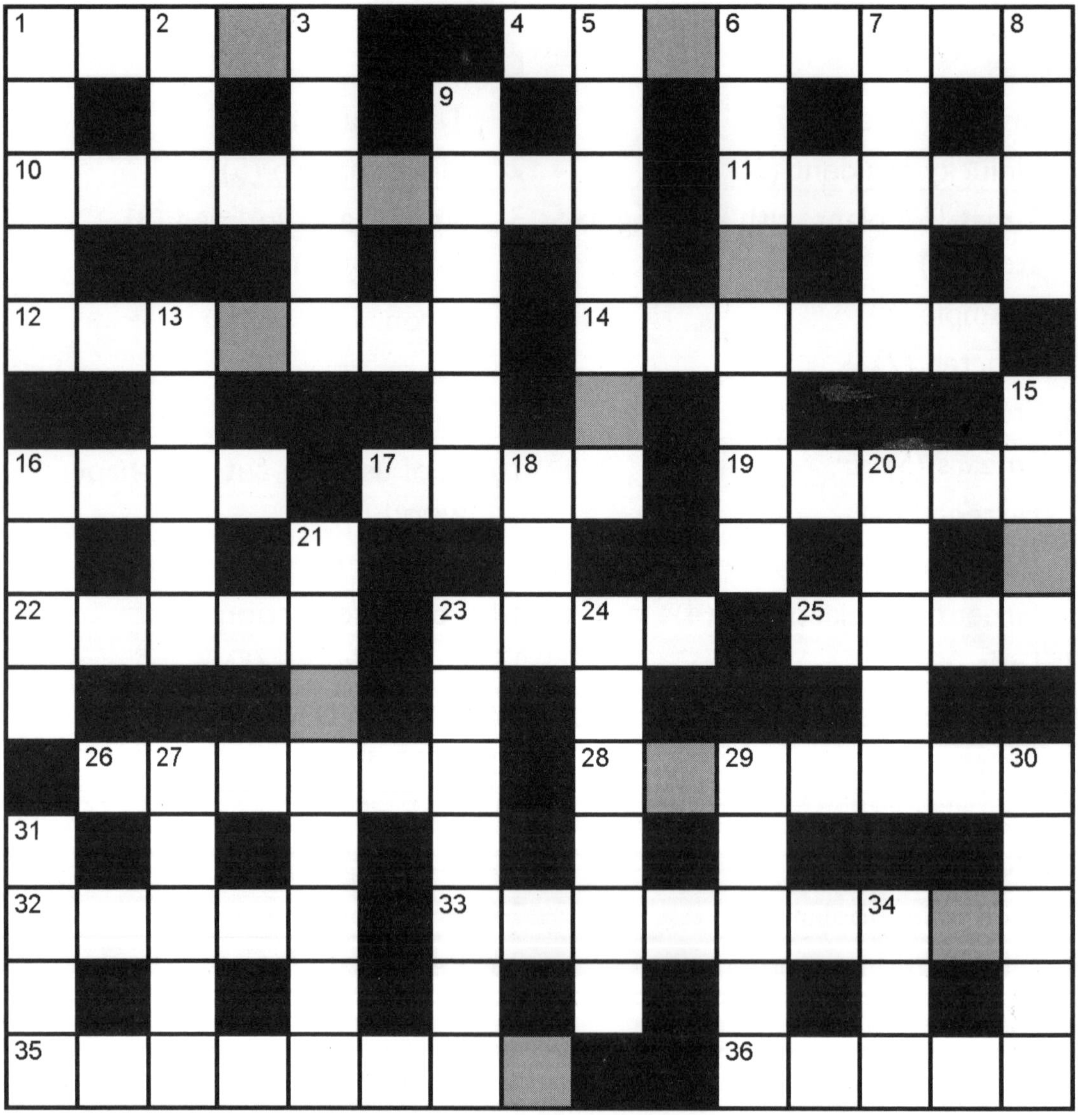

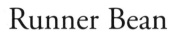

When the crossword is completed, the shaded squares will spell out the name of a variety of runner bean.

Across

1 Land through which the Nile flows (5)
4 Non-professionals (8)
10 A pen drips (anagram) – wading bird (9)
11 Barnaby ___ (Dickens novel) (5)
12 Deciduous shrub from China with panicles of white or pink flowers (7)
14 Cricket arbiter (6)
16 Johann Sebastian ___ (composer) (4)
17 German river (4)
19 Shared fund of money (5)
22 In that place (5)
23 Female pigs (4)
25 On a single occasion (4)
26 A flowing in (6)
28 Provider of refreshments (7)
32 When expected (2,3)
33 All people (9)
35 Close investigation (8)
36 Aggregate (5)

Down

1 Alleviated (5)
2 Hankering (3)
3 Precious stone (5)
5 Large tent (7)
6 Toll road (8)
7 Beneath (5)
8 Look for (4)
9 Lie with limbs spread out (6)
13 Male relative (5)
15 Isle of Wight town (4)
16 Mouthful (4)
18 Frightening word? (3)
20 Male singing voice (5)
21 Recklessly determined (8)
23 Four squared (7)
24 Evil (6)
27 More pleasant (5)
29 Assignation (5)
30 Regal, majestic (5)
31 Raining cats and ___ (4)
34 Pricking ___ (transplanting and spacing seedlings) (3)

Garden Assortment

Eight of the clues in this crossword (the ones in capital letters) are anagrams of the names of garden plants. Simply shuffle the letters to find the answers.

Across

1 BESTIAL (7)
5 RACED (5)
8 AMPLE (5)
9 Edible shellfish (7)
10 Kerfuffle (2-2)
12 Title of Russian emperors (4)
14 Not on (3)
15 ALLURE (6)
18 ELATES (6)
21 Container, as for compost (3)
22 Haul (4)
23 Cuts the grass (4)
27 Put back (7)
30 STARE (5)
31 CILLA (5)
32 ASYLUMS (7)

Down

1 Let in (5)
2 Lukewarm (5)
3 White-stemmed vegetable (4)
4 Self-centred person (6)
5 Variety of lettuce (3)
6 Owing (3)
7 Tranquil (7)
11 Rower's implement (3)
13 Strong-smelling perennial herb (3)
14 Operations (abbreviated) (3)
15 Generous (7)
16 Vase (3)
17 Finish (3)
19 Limb (3)
20 Device for taking photographs (6)
24 Sworn promises (5)
25 Hop it (5)
26 Simple (4)
28 Friend (3)
29 Curve (3)

63

Unseasonal Weather

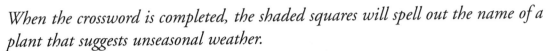

When the crossword is completed, the shaded squares will spell out the name of a plant that suggests unseasonal weather.

Across

1 Establish (3,2)
4 Plentiful (8)
10 Greenish blue (9)
11 "Aida" composer (5)
12 The Big Apple (3,4)
14 Japanese robe (6)
16 Come into contact with (4)
17 The part of a leaf that conveys fluids (4)
18 Occurrence (5)
21 Perfume (5)
22 Gaffer (4)
24 Type of steak (4)
25 Style of art associated with Picasso (6)
27 Item of clothing (7)
31 Sharp (5)
32 Mementos (9)
34 Erasing (8)
35 Saltpetre (5)

Down

1 Lustrous fabric (5)
2 Seaman (3)
3 One of the planets (5)
5 Enter forcibly (5,2)
6 Winter month (8)
7 Elder brother of Moses (5)
8 Remove excess from (4)
9 Inconstant (6)
13 A question of place? (5)
15 Pace (4)
16 Vertical spar for supporting sails (4)
19 Avoid (5)
20 Unpleasantly loud and harsh (8)
22 Yokel (7)
23 Seal (6)
26 Customary (5)
28 Ascended (5)
29 Flavour (5)
30 Female servant (4)
33 Equipment (3)

Lettuce

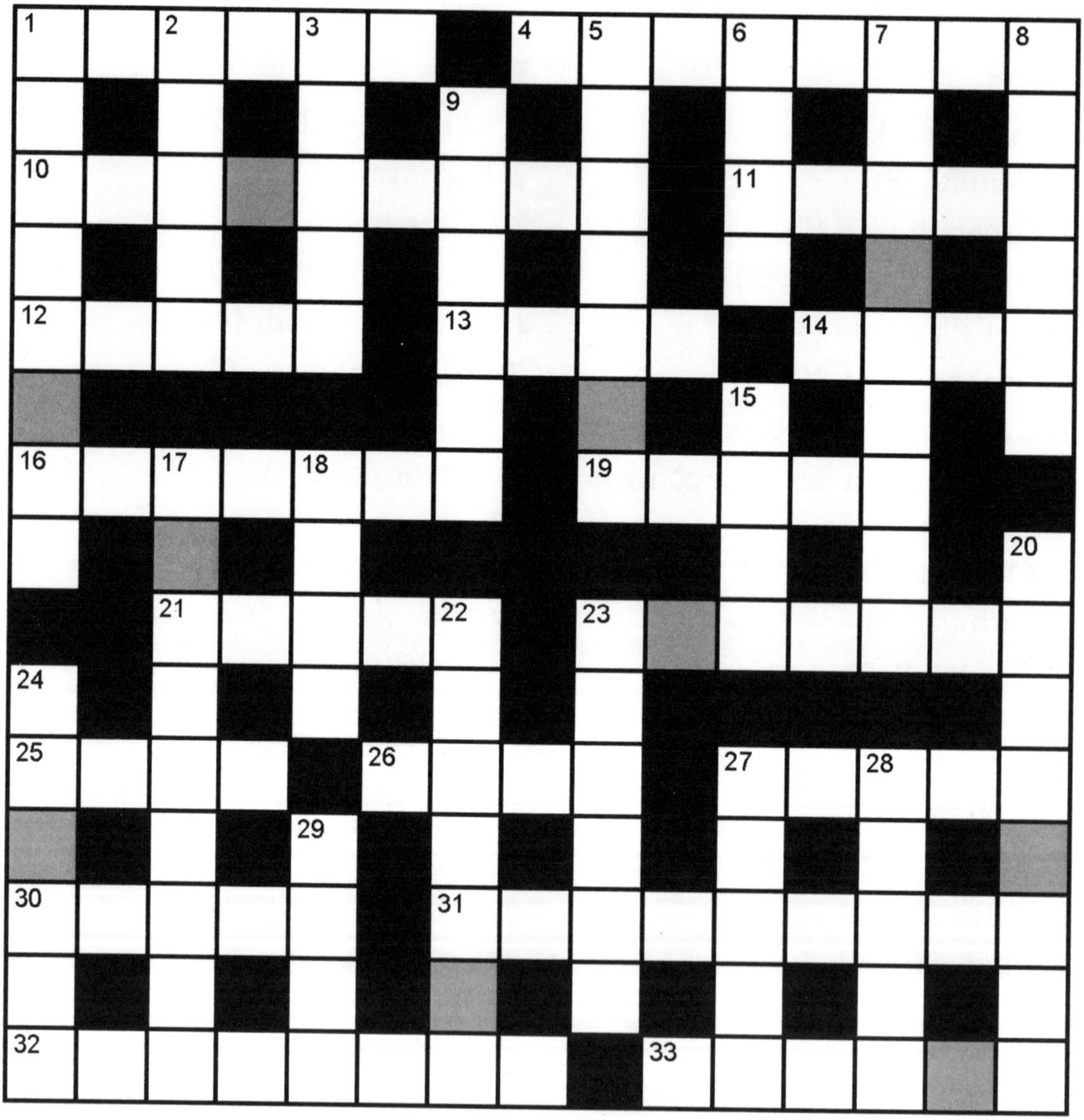

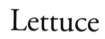

*When the crossword is completed, the shaded squares will spell out
the name of a variety of lettuce.*

Across

1   Be unsteady on one's feet (6)
4   Tree or shrub not trained on an
    espalier or a wall (8)
10 An impulse (anagram) –
    spleenwort (9)
11 Pleasing sounds (5)
12 Effervescent (5)
13 Author unknown (4)
14 Chilled (4)
16 Charged with an offence (7)
19 Agreeable odour (5)
21 Move furtively (5)
23 Aridity (7)
25 Twelvemonth (4)
26 Practise boxing (4)
27 "La Traviata" composer (5)
30 Snapshot (5)
31 Omission (9)
32 Okayed (8)
33 Slow sentimental song (6)

Down

1   Linaria, a flower related to the
    snapdragon (8)
2   Yellow precious stone (5)
3   Sorrowful poem (5)
5   Lottery (7)
6   Lacking feeling (4)
7   Colleague (9)
8   Resolve (6)
9   Magician (6)
15 Sacred (4)
17 In exultant spirits (4-1-4)
18 Large round basket of
    wickerwork or straw (4)
20 Aided (8)
22 Red Indian child (7)
23 English county (6)
24 Nearsightedness (6)
27 Prospect (5)
28 Royal, majestic (5)
29 Extinct bird (4)

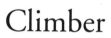

Climber

¹		²		³			⁴	⁵		⁶		⁷		⁸

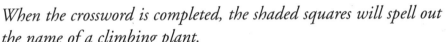

*When the crossword is completed, the shaded squares will spell out
the name of a climbing plant.*

Across

I   Over there (6)

4   London airport (8)

10   Exposed (9)

11   Dutch cheese (5)

12   Conjecture (5)

13   Necessity (4)

14   Prepare for publication (4)

16   Tipsy (7)

19   Revel (5)

21   Quilt (5)

23   South American country (7)

25   Ripped (4)

26   Preserved (4)

27   Reasoned thinking (5)

30   Perfect (5)

31   Fine porcelain (4,5)

32   Horticulturist (8)

33   Method (6)

Down

I   Least advanced in age (8)

2   Mother-of-pearl (5)

3   Overhanging roof edges (5)

5   Interminable (7)

6   Roman garment (4)

7   Cavalier's foe (9)

8   Riches (6)

9   Spirit distilled from wine (6)

15   Language of Pakistan (4)

17   Lingerie (9)

18   Number in a quintet (4)

20   Announce (8)

22   Quiver (7)

23   Stretch out (6)

24   Cord (6)

27   Fortunate (5)

28   Corn for grinding (5)

29   Run away (4)

Shrub

When the crossword is completed, the shaded squares will spell out the name of a flowering shrub.

Across

1 ___ mulberry (Morus nigra) (5)
4 The small hard seeds of a fleshy fruit (4)
6 Woodwind instrument (4)
10 Gross mistake (7)
11 Weave, interlace (7)
12 Whirlpool (4)
13 Parasitic insect (4)
14 Former Turkish title of those in high office (5)
16 Not suitable for eating (8)
18 Confronted (5)
20 Ernie (anagram) – girl's name (5)
21 Broadcasting (2,3,3)
22 Pays a visit (5)
25 Chop roughly (4)
27 Bogus (4)
30 Fishing vessel (7)
31 Compensation (7)
32 Manure (4)
33 Ancient string instrument with curved arms (4)
34 Prose composition (5)

Down

1 Holy Writ (5)
2 Plentiful supply (9)
3 Children (4)
4 Danger (5)
5 Widespread (9)
7 Great happiness (5)
8 Green gem (7)
9 Desist (4)
15 Tool for cutting and shaping wood (4)
17 Fraternal (9)
18 Perceive by touch (4)
19 Nicest ash (anagram) – former Scottish county (9)
20 Instigated (7)
23 Gain knowledge (5)
24 Grain store (4)
26 Line that isn't straight (5)
28 Untidy (5)
29 Slight competitive advantage (4)

Artist

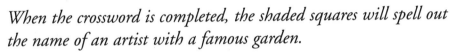

When the crossword is completed, the shaded squares will spell out the name of an artist with a famous garden.

Across

1 Sorceress (5)
4 Vow (4)
6 Bathroom powder (4)
10 Teach (7)
11 Equivalent word (7)
12 Mark as correct or complete (4)
13 Walk through shallow water (4)
14 More judicious (5)
16 Container resulting from a successfully fertilised flower (8)
18 Rot (5)
20 Imagine (5)
21 One who makes a will (8)
22 Not married (5)
25 Depose (4)
27 Flower containers (4)
30 Framework for climbing plants (7)
31 Put right (7)
32 Cummerbund (4)
33 Put away for storage (4)
34 Topic (5)

Down

1 Cereal crop (5)
2 Policeman's club (9)
3 Cure (4)
4 Madam Butterfly, for example (5)
5 Insipid (9)
7 Female relatives (5)
8 Plant with hairy leaves used in herbal medicine (7)
9 Nibble at (4)
15 Momentous date in World War II (1-3)
17 Space traveller (9)
18 Small drink of alcohol (4)
19 Aquatic reptile (9)
20 Blunder (4,3)
23 Merchandise (5)
24 Arab boat (4)
26 Prison officer (slang) (5)
28 Characteristic manner (5)
29 Rabbit's tail (4)

Pond Plant

74

When the crossword is completed, the shaded squares will spell out the name of a variety of pond plant.

Across

1 Savour (5)
4 The first man (4)
7 Started (3)
10 True to life (9)
11 Free from obstructions (5)
12 Fatuous (5)
14 Goal (3)
15 Florida resort (5)
16 Swiftly (7)
18 Stroll (7)
20 Appease, pacify (7)
22 Bird found in Antarctic regions (7)
24 Trembling poplar (5)
26 Greek woodland god (3)
27 For a particular purpose only (2,3)
28 Ceasefire (5)
30 Now and again (9)
32 Disencumbered (3)
33 Ill-mannered (4)
34 Spanish wine (5)

Down

1 Breed of dog (7)
2 Health resort (3)
3 Chosen few (5)
5 Absconds (7)
6 Raincoat (3)
7 Aida, for example (5)
8 One who shoes horses (7)
9 Regular boyfriend or girlfriend (6)
13 Greek vowel (5)
15 Grieve over (5)
17 Attracted (5)
19 Robust (5)
20 Large dish (7)
21 Uncovered (7)
22 Central American canal (6)
23 Capital of Cyprus (7)
25 Batter (5)
27 Modify (5)
29 Go astray (3)
31 China's "Great Helmsman" (3)

Thorny

When the crossword is completed, the shaded squares will spell out the name of a thorny shrub.

Across

1 List of things to be done or discussed (6)
4 Sad (7)
9 Puzzled (9)
10 Windproof jacket (5)
11 Called (5)
12 Told porkies (4)
13 Hard or exhausting labour (4)
15 Mariners (7)
18 Detached piece of a plant for propagating (5)
20 All thumbs (5)
22 Student (7)
24 Finished (4)
25 Ballet dancer's skirt (4)
26 Dark fur (5)
29 Anger (5)
30 Obstinate (9)
31 Type of light bulb fitting (7)
32 Rapid (6)

Down

1 Reprove (8)
2 Surrey racecourse (5)
3 Desiccated (5)
4 Strip (7)
5 They give beer its bitter taste (4)
6 Staff (9)
7 Annually (6)
8 Gangways (6)
14 Wealthy (4)
16 Travel plan (9)
17 Comply with orders (4)
19 Amiable (8)
21 Wind instrument (7)
22 Euphorbia (6)
23 It's built by a spider (6)
26 Farm animals (5)
27 Move (5)
28 Part of a leg (4)

Tulip

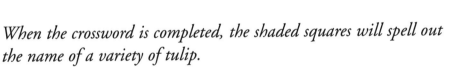

When the crossword is completed, the shaded squares will spell out the name of a variety of tulip.

Across

1   Small flute (7)
5   Young children (6)
8   Motionless (5)
9   Aquatic reptile (9)
11 Seven days (4)
12 Piece of money (4)
13 Weary (5)
15 Outlaw of Sherwood (5)
17 Memento (8)
20 Prior (8)
21 Preliminary period (3-2)
24 Garden tools (5)
26 Slices (4)
27 Equitable (4)
30 One side of a ship (9)
31 Florida resort (5)
32 A sculptor's work (6)
33 Low stuffed seat (7)

Down

1   After 1945 (7)
2   South American country (5)
3   Painting medium (4)
4   Public speaker (6)
5   Stable – poised (8)
6   Intolerant person (5)
7   Divert (9)
10 Raised strip (5)
14 Opposed (4)
16 Morning meal (9)
18 Pleasure garden (4)
19 Buy (8)
20 French capital (5)
22 Breed of cat (7)
23 Artist's workroom (6)
25 Wooden shoe (5)
28 Fear-stricken state (5)
29 Overlook (4)

Potato

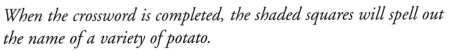

When the crossword is completed, the shaded squares will spell out the name of a variety of potato.

Across

1 Assists (5)
4 Section of a book (7)
9 In Australia or New Zealand (4,5)
10 Insipid (5)
11 Oval shape (7)
13 Academy awards (6)
15 Scottish lake (4)
16 ___ Laurel (comic actor) (4)
17 Hackneyed (5)
20 Thespian (5)
21 Corner (4)
23 Couple (4)
24 Artificial waterways (6)
26 Underground cell (7)
30 Employees (5)
31 Easily angered (9)
33 Colonist (7)
34 Soft or heavy with moisture (5)

Down

1 Line of shrubs (5)
2 Legislation (3)
3 Depression (5)
4 Humorous drawing (7)
5 Recommend (8)
6 Become narrower (5)
7 Unmannerly (4)
8 Period before Christmas (6)
12 Lawful (5)
14 Source of venison (4)
15 Rich soil consisting of sand, clay and organic material (4)
18 Senseless (5)
19 Awful (8)
21 More unpleasant (7)
22 Severe trial (6)
25 Asunder (5)
27 Small cuts (5)
28 Indigent, penurious (5)
29 Functions (4)
32 Large (3)

Fruit Garden

NECTARINE
DAMSON
CHERRY
GREENGAGE
STRAWBERRY
GOOSEBERRY
APPLE

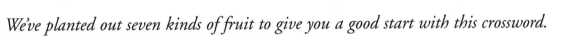

We've planted out seven kinds of fruit to give you a good start with this crossword.

Across

1 Imitate (5)
4 Tidal current (4)
6 ___ in the belfry (4)
10 FRUIT (9)
11 Change (5)
12 FRUIT (6)
13 One way or another (7)
17 Resist (6)
19 Buy (8)
20 Feel lash (anagram) – creeping perennial plant (4-4)
22 Missive (6)
24 Stabbing weapon (7)
26 FRUIT (6)
29 Ransack (5)
31 FRUIT (9)
32 American (4)
33 Prison (slang) (4)
34 Abate (3,2)

Down

1 List of choices (4)
2 Holy city of Islam (5)
3 Car frame (7)
4 Rule (5)
5 Game played on a checkered board (5)
7 Suitable (3)
8 FRUIT (10)
9 Road-surfacing material (6)
14 Centre (5)
15 FRUIT (10)
16 FRUIT (5)
18 Friendly (5)
21 Impede (6)
23 Everlasting (7)
25 Taut (5)
26 Free of obstructions (5)
27 Respond (5)
28 Retain (4)
30 Amusement (3)

Winter Colour

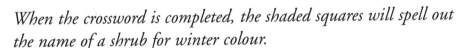

When the crossword is completed, the shaded squares will spell out the name of a shrub for winter colour.

Across

1 Garbage (5)
4 Clamber (8)
10 Wrong (9)
11 Sharp hooked claw (5)
12 Face-cloth (7)
14 Plant that completes its life cycle in one year (6)
16 Child's bed (4)
17 Formerly (4)
18 Rescued (5)
21 One of the five senses (5)
22 Afrikaans speaker (4)
24 Cans (4)
25 Obsolete gold coin (6)
27 Diversity (7)
31 Herb for Mr Fawlty? (5)
32 Instrument for measuring atmospheric pressure (9)
34 Drawn out (8)
35 Tales (5)

Down

1 Rich man, poor man, beggar man, ___ (5)
2 Alphabetical guide (3)
3 Wading bird with long legs (5)
5 Humble dwelling (7)
6 Amaze (8)
7 Strong very light wood (5)
8 Sea-eagle (4)
9 King Arthur's magician (6)
13 Farewell (5)
15 Poems (4)
16 Moggies (4)
19 Give utterance to (5)
20 Isle of Wight resort (8)
22 Blackberry bush (7)
23 Young eels (6)
26 Distressed (5)
28 Card game (5)
29 World War I battle (5)
30 Competent (4)
33 Rocky height (3)

Clematis

1		2		3		4	5		6		7		8

When the crossword is completed, the shaded squares will spell out the name of a variety of clematis.

Across

1   Divide by two (5)
4   Item of luggage (8)
10 Make laws (9)
11 Glowing coal (5)
12 Beginning of time (4,3)
14 Natural tooth covering (6)
16 Roald ___ (children's author) (4)
17 Loch __ monster (4)
19 English county (5)
22 Fragrant herb (5)
23 Changed colour (4)
25 Final (4)
26 Encumbrance (6)
28 Make haste (5,2)
32 Prohibited (5)
33 Laid bare (9)
35 Rock plants with violet or blue trumpet-shaped flowers (8)
36 Fast (5)

Down

1   Prickly evergreen shrub (5)
2   Record (3)
3   Relieved (5)
5   Futile (7)
6   Young person (8)
7   Saunter (5)
8   Multi-national currency (4)
9   Farm livestock (6)
13 ___ and pains (5)
15 Go out (4)
16 Money owing (4)
18 Secret agent (3)
20 Frightening (5)
21 Perennials with brightly coloured flower spikes (8)
23 Philanderer (3,4)
24 Code of behaviour (6)
27 Of the town (5)
29 Large crow (5)
30 Tantrum (5)
31 Adult male deer (4)
34 Sharp tap (3)

Shrub

*When the crossword is completed, the shaded squares will spell out
the name of a colourful shrub.*

Across

1. Morning glory (7)
5. Noon (6)
8. Pretend (5)
9. Owned up (9)
11. Exposed (4)
12. Determination (4)
13. Also-ran (5)
15. Vestige (5)
17. Hot spell (4,4)
20. Sweat (8)
21. Rise (3,2)
24. Water ___ (Geum rivale) (5)
26. Moderately cold (4)
27. Adjoin (4)
30. Arduous, toilsome (9)
31. Once more (5)
32. Brutes (6)
33. Posy (7)

Down

1. Ahead (2,5)
2. Yellowish-green colour (5)
3. Possesses (4)
4. Pact (6)
5. Troubadour (8)
6. Reside (5)
7. Helper (9)
10. Funeral song (5)
14. Military vehicle (4)
16. Pleasant (9)
18. Republic in West Africa (4)
19. Cherished (8)
20. Precious stone (5)
22. Power (7)
23. Venom (6)
25. Categories (5)
28. Melvyn ___ (novelist and TV presenter) (5)
29. Girl (4)

Celebrity Gardener

1
2
3
4
5
6
7
8
9
10
11
12
13
14
15
16
17
18
19
20
21
22
23
24
25
26
27
28
29
30
31
32
33
34

When the crossword is completed, the shaded squares will spell out the name of a celebrity gardener.

Across

1 Longest river in France (5)
4 Piece of work (4)
6 Fish related to the herring (4)
10 Disgrace (7)
11 Condiment made with fruit, chillies, etc. (7)
12 Father (4)
13 Elegantly stylish (4)
14 Weighty (5)
16 1815 battle (8)
18 Stiff (5)
20 Given medicine (5)
21 Under an obligation (8)
22 Hereditary class in India (5)
25 Genuine (4)
27 Male deer (4)
30 Fetched (7)
31 Soothing (7)
32 Mere (4)
33 Prepare for publication (4)
34 Resided (5)

Down

1 Endures (5)
2 Behind with payments (2,7)
3 Terminates (4)
4 Cultivated land (5)
5 Penitential attire (9)
7 Hair dye (5)
8 Tearless (3-4)
9 Hurry (4)
15 Nourish (4)
17 Set free (9)
18 Annoy (4)
19 Pomegranate syrup (9)
20 Measure of noise intensity (7)
23 Loose garment (5)
24 Poultry products (4)
26 Surrey racecourse (5)
28 Blotto (5)
29 Clothed (4)

Colourful Perennial

When the crossword is completed, the shaded squares will spell out the name of a colourful perennial.

Across

1 Drying cloth (5)
4 Certain (4)
6 Poems (4)
10 Morning glory (7)
11 Wash (7)
12 False statements (4)
13 Civil disorder (4)
14 Bind (3,2)
15 Scented (8)
18 Fittingly (5)
20 Large stringed instrument (5)
21 Not fully developed (8)
23 Run away to be wed (5)
25 Deceptive trick (4)
26 Heap (4)
29 Adage (7)
30 Immediate (7)
31 Uncommon (4)
32 Adult male deer (4)
33 Type of beer mug (5)

Down

1 Spin round (5)
2 Type of flour (9)
3 Weaving frame (4)
4 Sports arena (7)
5 Having a family connection (7)
7 Evade (5)
8 Obstreperous (7)
9 Take away (8)
16 Blossomed (8)
17 Type of tree (3)
19 Bring to an end (9)
20 Less expensive (7)
21 Occupy (7)
22 Signification (7)
24 Smell (5)
27 Consumed (5)
28 Functions, purposes (4)

Fuchsia

94

*When the crossword is completed, the shaded squares will spell out
the name of a variety of fuchsia.*

Across

1   Electrical connection (5)
4   Religious observance (4)
6   Small piece of ground (4)
10 Chivalrous, dashing (7)
11 Three-pronged spear (7)
12 Diplomacy (4)
13 Whisky mixer (4)
14 Barrier of wood or wood and wire (5)
16 Former French prison (8)
18 Famous diarist (5)
20 Private instructor (5)
21 One of the Channel Islands (8)
22 Hard dark wood (5)
25 Band worn round the waist or over the shoulder (4)
27 Colour of unbleached linen (4)
30 Ice-cream flavour (7)
31 Letters in sloping type (7)
32 Egyptian canal (4)
33 Chief of the Greek gods (4)
34 Vision (5)

Down

1   Rowing crew (5)
2   Disinclined (9)
3   Warmth (4)
4   Proportion (5)
5   Private conversation between two people (4-1-4)
7   Stay in bed longer (3,2)
8   Shreds (7)
9   Petty quarrel (4)
15 Heavenly light (4)
17 Make laws (9)
18 Small horse (4)
19 Delivering sermons (9)
20 Dozens (7)
23 Light weight (5)
24 Shout (4)
26 From Switzerland (5)
28 Capsize (5)
29 ___ and means (4)

Rock Plant

1		2		3				4		5		6		7
9									10				
11		12				13				14				
15				16				17				18		
19						20		21						22
23		24				25				26				
27				28		29						30		
31									32				

When the crossword is completed, the shaded squares will spell out the name of a popular rock plant.

Across

1 Flavoured milk drink (5)
4 Resisted (7)
9 Wreathed in flowers (9)
10 Robber (5)
11 Eject (5)
13 Hot beverage (3)
14 Conjuring (5)
15 Gland in the neck (7)
17 Stray from the subject (7)
19 Foes (7)
21 One of the gospels (7)
23 Scholarly books (5)
25 Edge (3)
26 Spooky (5)
27 ___ Moser, popular variety of clematis (5)
29 Conserve made from oranges (9)
31 Despotism (7)
32 Woollen material (5)

Down

1 Propose (7)
2 Make public (3)
3 Electronic communication (1-4)
4 Experienced person (3,4)
5 Marijuana (3)
6 Item of playground equipment (5)
7 Flaws (7)
8 Prepared for publication (6)
12 Person paid (5)
14 Power (5)
16 Leaves out (5)
18 Anaesthetic (5)
19 Defunct (7)
20 Rough cider (7)
21 Recollection (6)
22 Saturday and Sunday (7)
24 Middle-distance runner (5)
26 Accurate (5)
28 Japanese currency (3)
30 Imitate (3)

Back of the Border

When the crossword is completed, the shaded squares will spell out the name of a plant that's ideal for the back of the border.

Across

1 Use a loom (5)
4 Dutch cheese (4)
6 Circle (4)
10 Dwell in (7)
11 Aged between 12 and 20 (7)
12 Mountain lake (4)
13 Scheme (4)
14 Eskimo canoe (5)
16 Broken down, worn out (8)
18 Meat from a pig (5)
20 Performed in a play (5)
21 Object believed to have magic powers (8)
22 Accommodation for prisoners (5)
25 Greasy (4)
27 Hairdo (4)
30 Haven (7)
31 Increase (7)
32 Heather (4)
33 Thin fog (4)
34 Alleviated (5)

Down

1 Popular card game (5)
2 Repugnant (9)
3 German river (4)
4 Eulogise (5)
5 Before birth (9)
7 European country (5)
8 Small cucumber used for pickling (7)
9 Summit (4)
15 Small nail (4)
17 Fragrant mixture of dried leaves and petals (9)
18 Deep-voiced male singer (4)
19 Unending (9)
20 Intoxicating liquor (7)
23 Sophia ___, film actress (5)
24 Sluggish (4)
26 Minimum (5)
28 Not loud (5)
29 Look at lasciviously (4)

Iris

When the crossword is completed, the shaded squares will spell out the name of a variety of iris.

Across

1   Knee bone (7)
5   Deposit that forms on teeth (6)
8   Narcotic derived from poppies (5)
9   Hermit (9)
11 Long slippery fish (4)
12 Half of a quart (4)
13 Located (5)
15 Young man (5)
17 One to whom money is owed (8)
20 Lady's ___ (Galium verum) (8)
21 Reside (5)
24 Not urban (5)
26 Defensive trench around a castle (4)
27 Raiment (4)
30 Callous (9)
31 Heather genus (5)
32 Tools for trimming lawn boundaries (6)
33 Incorrectly (7)

Down

1   Offspring (7)
2   Ordeal (5)
3   Linden (4)
4   Tender evergreen mimosa with yellow or white flowers (6)
5   Habitually silent (8)
6   Chambers (5)
7   Treat soil (anagram) – Greek philosopher (9)
10 Down-producing duck (5)
14 Informal conversation (4)
16 Sneaky (9)
18 Extinct bird (4)
19 Serenity (8)
20 Accommodation on ship (5)
22 Collection of books (7)
23 Poland's capital (6)
25 Supple (5)
28 Growing old (5)
29 Nil (4)

Birds in the Garden

BLACKBIRD
BLUETIT
ROBIN
WREN
SPARROW
CHAFFINCH
GULL

Don't disturb the birds!

Across

1 Bragged (7)
5 Stalk (4)
10 Michaelmas ___ (aster) (5)
11 GARDEN BIRD (9)
12 GARDEN BIRD (4,3)
14 Lack of moisture (7)
16 GARDEN BIRD (5)
18 Citizen of Denmark (4)
20 GARDEN BIRD (4)
23 Primitive aquatic plant (4)
25 Wild pig (4)
28 Citrus fruit (5)
30 Assert (7)
33 GARDEN BIRD (7)
35 GARDEN BIRD (9)
36 Command (5)
38 GARDEN BIRD (4)
39 Traveller to a holy place (7)

Down

1 Garden plot (3)
2 Au revoir (5)
3 Attempt (3)
4 Discussed (7)
6 Hungarian wine (5)
7 Corn (5)
8 Custodian (6)
9 Having a better than even chance (4-2)
12 Exclude (3)
13 Very small (4)
15 Novel (3)
17 Beseech (3)
19 ___ mode (1,2)
21 Odd (3)
22 Island to which Napoleon was exiled (4)
23 Kidnap (6)
24 Everything (3)
26 Large seas (6)
27 Berry-like fruit that can be used to make a kind of tea (7)
29 At this time (3)
31 Loud resonant noise (5)
32 Dire (5)
34 One on horseback (5)
36 Lubricate (3)
37 Male sheep (3)

Clematis

1
2
3
4
5
6
7
8
9
10
11
12
13
14
15
16
17
18
19
20
21
22
23
24
25
26
27
28
29
30
31
32
33

When the crossword is completed, the shaded squares will spell out the name of a variety of clematis.

Across

1 Witty saying (7)
5 Corsair (6)
8 Broadcasting medium (5)
9 Communicate successfully (3,6)
11 Cab (4)
12 Become active (4)
13 Insurgent (5)
15 Hidden store (5)
17 Cradle (8)
20 Delphinium (8)
21 Bewildered (2,3)
24 Endures (5)
26 Ireland, in poetry (4)
27 Female servant (4)
30 Bell-tower (9)
31 Sacred song (5)
32 One who attends to horses (6)
33 Design (7)

Down

1 Capricious (7)
2 Guide to book contents (5)
3 Quarter of an acre (4)
4 Powerful (6)
5 Fatherly (8)
6 Happen again (5)
7 Brass instruments (9)
10 Divide (5)
14 Wagers (4)
16 Winter festival (9)
18 Wet thoroughly (4)
19 Higher-ranking (8)
20 Fragrant shrub (5)
22 Midriff (7)
23 Surrender (4,2)
25 Shoulder-wrap (5)
28 Hard stone (5)
29 Spade's depth (4)

Sun Lover

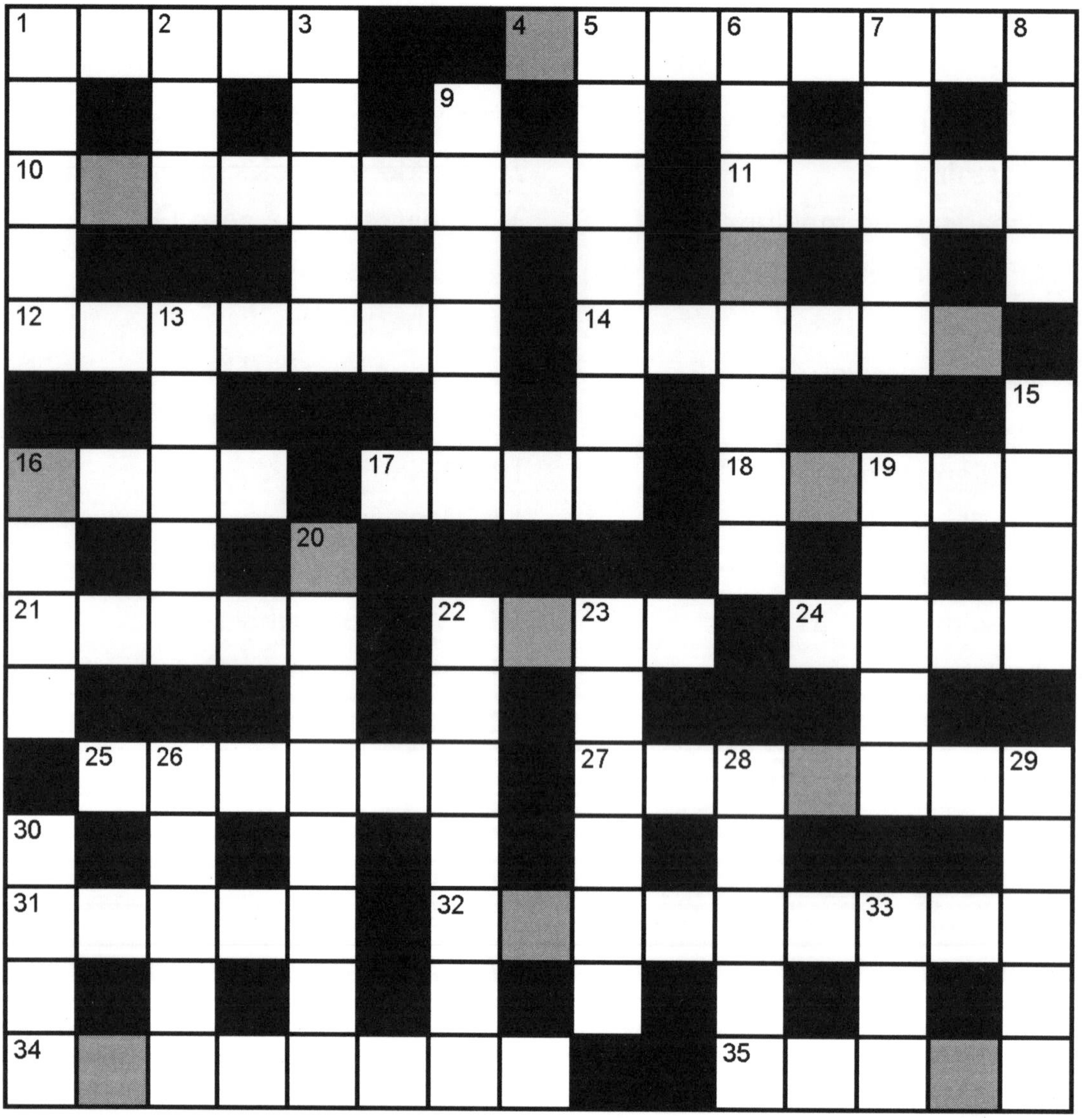

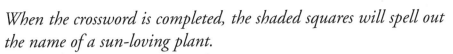

*When the crossword is completed, the shaded squares will spell out
the name of a sun-loving plant.*

Across

1   Climb (5)
4   Castigate (8)
10 Reckless person (9)
11 Bread maker (5)
12 Bullfighter (7)
14 Fair-haired (6)
16 Average (4)
17 Swag (4)
18 Mother-of-pearl (5)
21 Outcome (5)
22 The spongy cellular tissue inside
    the stems of plants (4)
24 Weapons (4)
25 Sister of Venus (6)
27 Mixed (7)
31 Praise highly (5)
32 Bearable (9)
34 Spanish music (8)
35 Coin-tossing call (5)

Down

1   Stonecrop (5)
2   Tune (3)
3   Finished (5)
5   Food fish (7)
6   Writ compelling attendance (8)
7   Irritated (5)
8   Republic of Ireland (4)
9   Exaggerate (6)
13 Rips (5)
15 A smaller amount (4)
16 Chain armour (4)
19 Shade of pink (5)
20 Wake-up call (8)
22 Synthetic material (7)
23 Uproar (6)
26 Minor actor in crowd scenes (5)
28 Compass bearing (5)
29 Slimming courses (5)
30 Unable to hear (4)
33 Sheep's cry (3)

Leek

When the crossword is completed, the shaded squares will spell out the name of a variety of leek.

Across

1 Ostentatious (5)
4 Having a fragrant smell (8)
10 Unwilling (9)
11 Fairy-tale monsters (5)
12 Long pillow (7)
14 Shored (anagram) – Greek island (6)
16 Highland dagger (4)
17 Burden, responsibility (4)
18 Deduce (5)
21 Natural aptitude (5)
22 Male rabbit (4)
24 Black bird (4)
25 Giant planet (6)
27 Change for the better (7)
31 Historical era (5)
32 Eggplant (9)
34 Completed (8)
35 Divisions of a bunch of bananas (5)

Down

1 Wash vigorously (5)
2 Pussycat's partner (3)
3 Sailing-boat (5)
5 Comes back (7)
6 Forget-me-not (8)
7 Concise, pithy (5)
8 Snug (4)
9 Infertile (6)
13 Immature form of insect (5)
15 Forehead (4)
16 Bonkers (4)
19 Waive (5)
20 Currents of air (8)
22 Slavery (7)
23 Ascends (6)
26 Bedeck (5)
28 Rod, pole or ___ (5)
29 Fencing swords (5)
30 Gripe, grouse (4)
33 Electrically charged particle (3)

Raspberry

When the crossword is completed, the shaded squares will spell out the name of a variety of raspberry.

Across

1 Fight off, drive back (5)
4 Wild horse (7)
9 Type of pen (9)
10 Defeated contestant (5)
11 Regard with favour (5,2)
13 To this place (6)
15 Pay a visit (4)
16 Roman god of war (4)
18 Enclosed kitchen fireplace (5)
21 Cuban dance (5)
22 Precious metal (4)
24 Common sense (4)
25 Water ice (6)
27 Language of East Africa (7)
31 Deduce (5)
32 Celebrated (4-5)
34 Curtly (7)
35 Broader (5)

Down

1 Picture puzzle (5)
2 Chum (3)
3 Mistake resulting from inattention (5)
4 Competitive games (7)
5 Alone, without company (8)
6 Gangway (5)
7 Young lady (4)
8 Austrian capital (6)
12 Muslim religion (5)
14 Optical glass (4)
15 Heart (4)
17 Brazilian city (3)
19 ___ Campbell, supermodel (5)
20 Scout rally (8)
22 Escape (7)
23 Finally (6)
26 Tender (5)
28 Awry (5)
29 Part of a target next to the bull's-eye (5)
30 Elevator (4)
33 Aged (3)

National Trust

112

*When the crossword is completed, the shaded squares will spell out
the name of an outstanding National Trust garden.*

Across

1 Put in sequence (5)

4 Sodium chloride (4)

6 Unhearing (4)

10 Wind-storm (7)

11 English cheese (7)

12 "A ___ by any other name..." (4)

13 Thought (4)

14 Tropical fruit often made into jelly (5)

15 East European country (8)

18 Boldness (5)

20 Viper (5)

21 Evaluate (8)

23 Instruct (5)

25 Spoken exam (4)

26 Aid in crime (4)

29 Island in the Atlantic off north-west Africa (7)

30 Mathematical proposition (7)

31 Conservative (4)

32 Verse composition (4)

33 Wood nymph (5)

Down

1 Academy award (5)

2 Sausage dog (9)

3 ___ stock, a plant onto which another variety is grafted (4)

4 Gracefully slim (7)

5 Milan opera house (2,5)

7 Accessory (5)

8 Flourish of trumpets (7)

9 ___ creeper (Parthenocissus) (8)

16 "Rhapsody in Blue" composer (8)

17 Little devil (3)

19 Soft fruit (9)

20 Endeavour (7)

21 Savoury pear-shaped fruit (7)

22 Apparition (7)

24 Tree related to the birch (5)

27 Faint-hearted (5)

28 Take notice of (4)

Decorative Tree

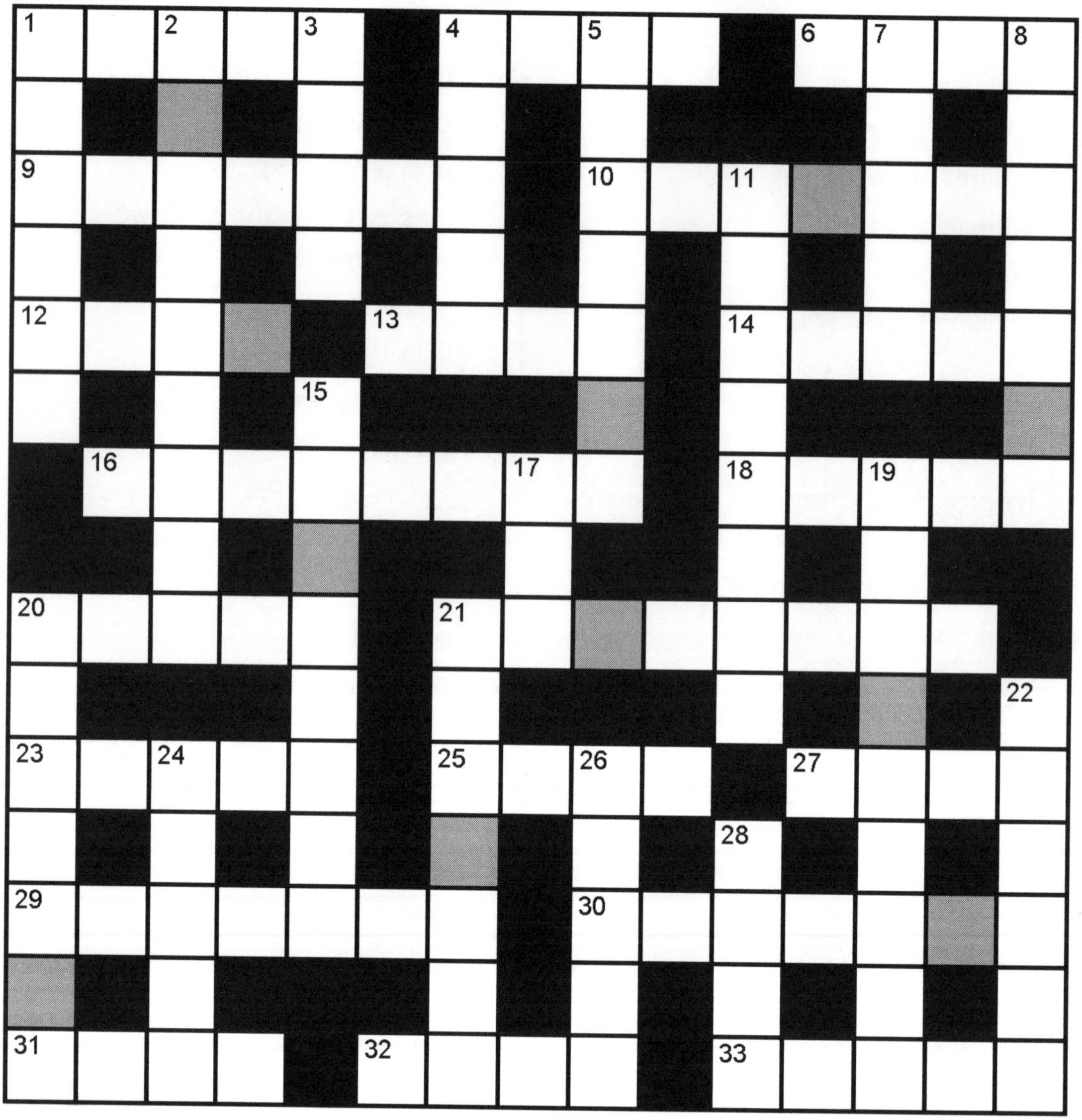

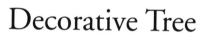

When the crossword is completed, the shaded squares will spell out the name of a decorative garden tree.

Across

1 Thoughts (5)
4 One of the four evangelists (4)
6 Deep open cut (4)
9 Water tank (7)
10 Endurance (7)
12 Staff carried as a nark of authority (4)
13 Siamese (4)
14 Circles (5)
16 Organism that lives on another, such as mistletoe (8)
18 The territory of a duke (5)
20 Freight (5)
21 Singer (8)
23 Type of parrot (5)
25 Ascend (4)
27 Carp, for example (4)
29 Trading ban (7)
30 Came in (7)
31 Always (4)
32 Skye, for example (4)
33 Legendary king with the golden touch (5)

Down

1 Earnings (6)
2 Comfortable seat (4,5)
3 Building possibly used for storing tools (4)
4 Bringer of bad luck (5)
5 Antagonistic (7)
7 Completely foreign (5)
8 Rumour (7)
11 Breed of terrier (8)
15 Old naval ship (3-2-3)
17 As well (3)
19 Dismissed from the armed services (9)
20 Host, master of ceremonies (7)
21 Sundry (7)
22 Sunglasses, colloquially (6)
24 Telegram (5)
26 Root vegetable (5)
28 Bit of news (4)

Bonsai

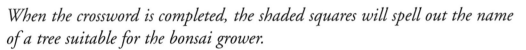

When the crossword is completed, the shaded squares will spell out the name of a tree suitable for the bonsai grower.

Across

1   High level ground (7)
5   Bludgeoned (6)
8   Courage (5)
9   Invasive twining plant (8)
11   Old Testament book (4)
12   Counterfeit (4)
13   Fasten again (5)
15   Nutmeg or cinnamon, say (5)
17   Gifts (9)
19   Irreproachable (9)
22   Broom made of twigs (5)
24   Doctor's stand-in (5)
26   Quarter of an acre (4)
27   Among (4)
29   Copious (8)
30   Swelling (5)
31   Comment (6)
32   Scandinavian country (7)

Down

1   Ancient writing material (7)
2   Grown-up (5)
3   Broad-antlered animal (3)
4   Reproach (7)
5   Employees' restaurant (7)
6   Drain (5)
7   Atomic particles (9)
10   Ruler of Olympus (4)
14   Dry up, scorch (4)
16   Choleric (9)
18   Brass instrument (4)
19   Hairless (4)
20   Set aside for a specific purpose (7)
21   Espied (7)
23   Wednesday or thereabouts (7)
25   High-IQ organisation (5)
28   Mediterranean island (5)
30   Outlaw (3)

Sweet Pea

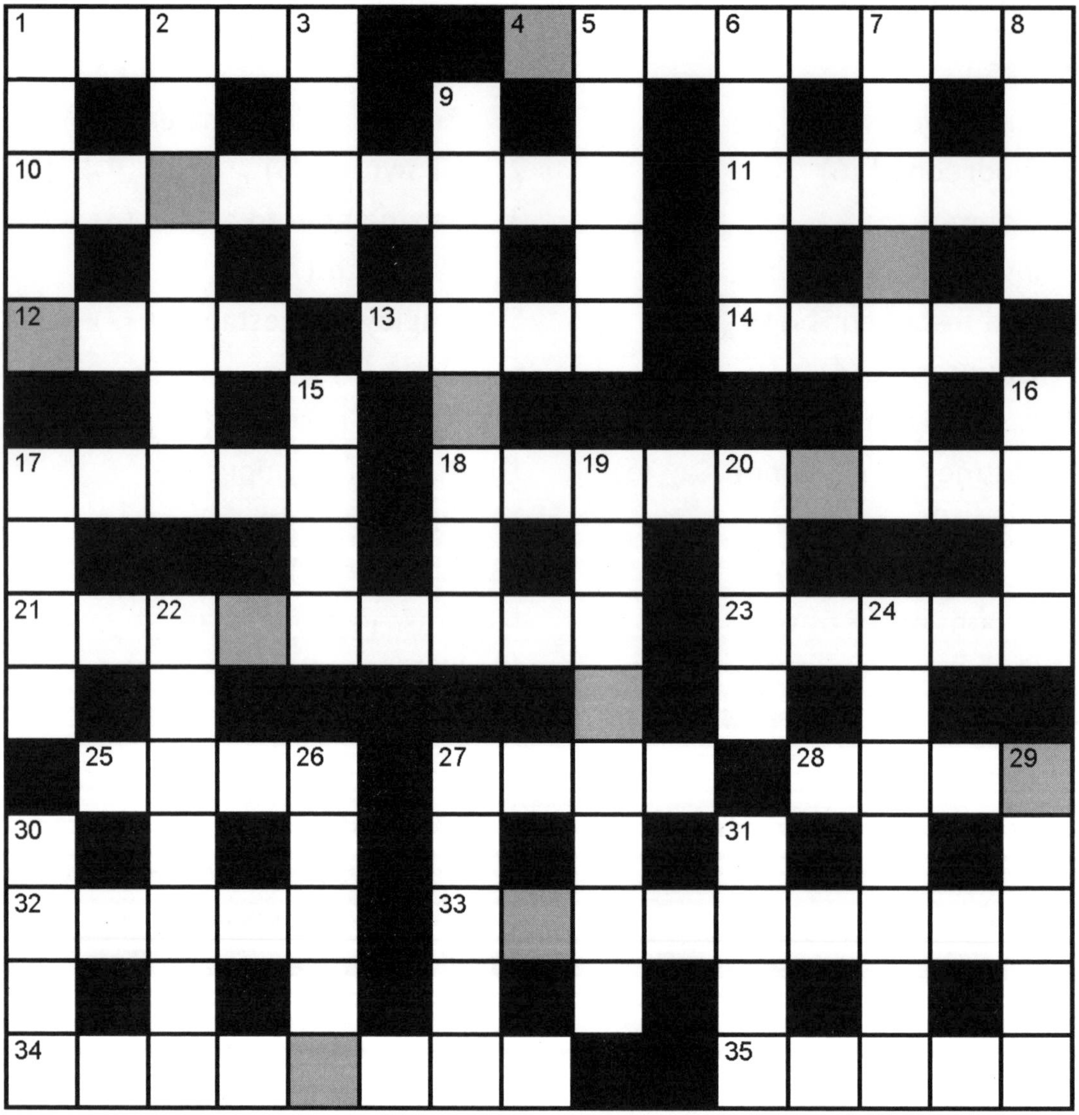

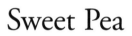

When the crossword is completed, the shaded squares will spell out the name of a variety of sweet pea.

Across

1 Lying face downward (5)
4 Free from obscurity (5-3)
10 Profusion (9)
11 Not clean (5)
12 Successes (4)
13 Nocturnal birds (4)
14 Haul (4)
17 Gasteropod mollusc – a common garden pest (5)
18 Prosperity (9)
21 Confused situation (9)
23 New (5)
25 A long time (4)
27 Frustrate (4)
28 Malay dagger with a wavy scalloped blade (4)
32 Check, examination (5)
33 Sweets on sticks (9)
34 Imperil (8)
35 Iron, for example (5)

Down

1 Velvety-skinned fruit (5)
2 Prickly-pear genus of the cactus family (7)
3 Stops (4)
5 Yorkshire city (5)
6 Assisted (5)
7 Sure (7)
8 Playthings (4)
9 Winter missile (8)
15 Singing voice (4)
16 Little ___ (Dickens heroine) (4)
17 Cutting (4)
19 Fleet of small ships (8)
20 Bone in the forearm (4)
22 Capital of Iraq (7)
24 US state (7)
26 Lustrous fabric (5)
27 Artificial (5)
29 Plant fibre used for making rope (5)
30 ___ gooseberry (Physalis edulis) (4)
31 Thailand, formerly (4)

Scottish Garden

When the crossword is completed, the shaded squares will spell out the name of a famous Scottish garden.

Across

1   ___ marigold (6)
4   Glorious (8)
10 Hunt alias (anagram) – tree of heaven (9)
11 Open space in a wood (5)
12 Legal right to ownership (5)
13 Wicked (4)
14 Item of footwear (4)
16 Full (of food) (7)
19 Wear away (5)
21 Regretting (5)
23 Husbands and wives (7)
25 Molten material from a volcano (4)
26 Modern Persia (4)
27 Forbidden (5)
30 Pursue (5)
31 Two weeks (9)
32 Catastrophe (8)
33 Woken up (6)

Down

1   Break (8)
2   Distinction (5)
3   Small boat (5)
5   Leisure activity (7)
6   Jittery (4)
7   Never dying (9)
8   Motor fuel (6)
9   Swiss ___ plant (Monstera deliciosa) (6)
15 Game played on horseback (4)
17 South Americans (9)
18 Way out (4)
20 Mixed (8)
22 Long-necked animal (7)
23 Soldier on watch (6)
24 Serene, unruffled (6)
27 Latin-American dance (5)
28 Sham (5)
29 Female birds (4)

Garden Girls

¹V	I	²O	L	³E	T			⁴	⁵		⁶		⁷L
						⁸		⁹					I
¹⁰									¹¹				L
													Y
¹²					¹³R	O	S	E	M	A	R	Y	
			¹⁴									¹⁵	
¹⁶P	A	N	S	Y			¹⁷		¹⁸				
					¹⁹								
²⁰		²¹						²²D	A	²³I	S	Y	
	²⁴H	Y	²⁵A	C	²⁶I	N	T	H		²⁷		²⁸	
²⁹I								³⁰					
³¹R				³²									
I													
³³S							³⁴L	A	U	R	E	L	

In this crossword we start you off with the names of eight garden
plants which are also girls' names.

Across

1 GIRL'S NAME (6)
4 Call off (6)
10 Staff (9)
11 Of the country (5)
12 Male sheep (4)
13 GIRL'S NAME (8)
16 GIRL'S NAME (5)
17 Entourage (7)
19 Choler (3)
20 Idle or wild fancy (7)
22 GIRL'S NAME (5)
24 GIRL'S NAME (8)
27 Hurt (4)
31 Luxurious car (5)
32 Writers of fiction (9)
33 Unhappier (6)
34 GIRL'S NAME (6)

Down

1 Adder (5)
2 Rower (7)
3 Greek god of love (4)
5 Main artery (5)
6 Continue (5,2)
7 GIRL'S NAME (4)
8 Prolonged inability to sleep (8)
9 Azure (4)
14 Kind, sort (4)
15 Exceedingly (4)
16 Select (4)
17 Not absolute (8)
18 Neat (4)
21 Breathed in (7)
23 Narrow-edged tooth (7)
25 Gangway (5)
26 Taverns (4)
28 Painter's stand (5)
29 GIRL'S NAME (4)
30 Supplication (4)

Parsnip

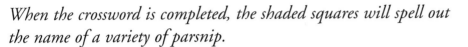

When the crossword is completed, the shaded squares will spell out the name of a variety of parsnip.

Across

1   Profundity (5)
4   Bird that sings aloft (4)
6   Church service (4)
10 Swindle (3)
11 Imitate (5)
12 Wear away (5)
13 Shake with cold (6)
14 Vindictive (8)
16 Former name of Iran (6)
17 Enclose (7)
20 Slices of bacon (7)
22 Ascending (6)
24 Lawyer (8)
27 Ludicrous (6)
30 Bart's father (5)
31 Higher (5)
32 Baby's bed (3)
33 Appointment (4)
34 Leading performer (4)
35 Unfortunately (5)

Down

1   ___ and drakes (5)
2   Destitute (9)
3   Picnic baskets (7)
4   Arm or leg (4)
5   Sum up (5)
7   Distant in manner (5)
8   Young plant (8)
9   Defeated (6)
15 ___ Domino (musician) (4)
17 Stiff paper (4)
18 Proclaimed (9)
19 Gave a sermon (8)
21 Mistakes (6)
23 Outer districts of town (7)
25 Entice (5)
26 Burst forth (5)
28 Simple song (5)
29 Incentive (4)

Evergreen Shrub

*When the crossword is completed, the shaded squares will spell out
the name of an evergreen shrub.*

Across

1   Own (7)
5   Tools for punching holes (4)
10 Cheap wine (5)
11 Invalidation (9)
12 Indian rice (7)
14 Outlandish (7)
16 Faux pas (5)
18 German art song (4)
20 The ___ House, a highlight of
    Kew Gardens (4)
23 Fruit with a stone (4)
25 Rouse (4)
28 Forsaken children (5)
30 Behind time for arrival (7)
33 Branch of mathematics (7)
35 Supreme (9)
36 Confess (5)
38 Hollow caused by a blow (4)
39 Make clear (7)

Down

1   Fizzy drink (3)
2   Exhibitions (5)
3   Large northern deer (3)
4   Alpines (anagram) – breed of dog (7)
6   Ballroom dance (5)
7   Daub (5)
8   Make possible (6)
9   Rivulet (6)
12 Insect (3)
13 Greek god of war (4)
15 Snake (3)
17 Common ailment (3)
19 Dark liquid ejected by a
    cuttlefish (3)
21 ___ Ward, gardening writer and
    TV presenter (3)
22 Small branch (4)
23 Punctual (6)
24 Spoil (3)
26 Tree-lined road (6)
27 Stretchy (7)
29 Mineral spring (3)
31 Made a mistake (5)
32 Evil spirit (5)
34 Disney deer (5)
36 ___ carte (1,2)
37 Endeavour (3)

Eastern Promise

When the crossword is completed, the shaded squares will spell out the name of a border plant that's full of eastern promise.

Across

1 Around-the-clock (7)
5 Archer's missile (5)
9 Greek letter S (5)
10 Columbine (9)
11 Greek resin-flavoured wine (7)
13 Torture (7)
15 Encounters (5)
17 Deserve by one's actions (4)
19 ___ Lizzie, indoor or outdoor plant (4)
21 Commanded (4)
22 Retail outlet (4)
25 Savoury jelly (5)
27 Warm and friendly (7)
29 Malicious gossip (7)
31 Bellflower (9)
33 Passenger ship (5)
34 Large bird of prey (5)
35 World's highest mountain (7)

Down

1 Favourite remedy or scheme (7)
2 Hours of darkness (5)
3 Earl Grey, for example (3)
4 Mollify (7)
5 More competent (5)
6 Scrap of cloth (3)
7 Affluent (7)
8 Six-stringed instrument (6)
12 The present month (abbr.) (4)
14 Fit out (5)
16 Small tree with purple fruit (5)
18 Bother (3)
20 Volcanic matter (4)
21 Two-wheeler (7)
23 Gas used in balloons (6)
24 Corridor (7)
26 Guilty party (7)
28 Likeness (5)
30 Thick (5)
32 Large cup (3)
33 Strong alkaline solution (3)

Gooseberry

When the crossword is completed, the shaded squares will spell out the name of a variety of gooseberry.

Across

1   Nelly ____, popular variety of clematis (5)
4   Precious stone (4)
6   Association (4)
10 Skin-tight garment (7)
11 Pungent gas (7)
12 Gardening tool (4)
13 Jupiter (4)
14 Devil (5)
16 Computer programs (8)
18 Boisterous (5)
20 Spice (5)
21 Former French prison (8)
22 Civilian dress (5)
25 Leader in a mosque (4)
27 Receptacle for rubbish (4)
30 Withdrawal (7)
31 Burdensome (7)
32 US coin (4)
33 Back of the neck (4)
34 Not relaxed (5)

Down

1   Back tooth (5)
2   Swedish capital (9)
3   Quantity of paper (4)
4   Exhibition of cowboy skills (5)
5   Innocent (9)
7   Flax (5)
8   Flattery or cajoling talk (7)
9   Among (4)
15 Stupefy (4)
17 Popular rockery plant (9)
18 Dilapidated building (4)
19 Familiar (4-5)
20 Fine white linen (7)
23 Belong (3,2)
24 Holly genus (4)
26 Make amends (5)
28 Adhesive (5)
29 Root vegetable providing sugar (4)

Easter

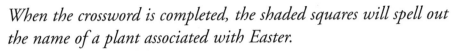

When the crossword is completed, the shaded squares will spell out the name of a plant associated with Easter.

Across

1 Seer (7)
5 Tuft of small flowers, as in the hazel, willow, etc. (6)
8 Many times (5)
9 Australian marsupials (9)
11 Steal (7)
12 Without weapons (7)
14 Wash in clean water (5)
16 Villein (4)
18 School class (4)
20 Blackthorn fruit (4)
21 Arduous journey (4)
24 Sharp or tapered end (5)
26 Replies (7)
28 Capital of Kenya (7)
30 Devoted (9)
32 Lifeless (5)
33 Handsome Greek god (6)
34 Fly south in winter (7)

Down

1 Thrive (7)
2 Exterior (5)
3 Morning-after malaise (8)
4 Cash receipts (7)
5 Vanquish (7)
6 Jewelled head ornament (5)
7 Wedding response (1,2)
10 Rock plant with white, yellow or pink flowers (5)
13 Native of New Zealand (5)
15 ___ and crannies (5)
17 Adam's mate (3)
19 Rebellion (8)
20 Injure with hot liquid (5)
22 Italian rice dish (7)
23 Monarchical state (7)
25 Prickly plant (7)
27 Outshine (5)
29 Greek vowel (5)
31 Immerse (3)

Topiary Garden

When the crossword is completed, the shaded squares will spell out the name of a famous topiary garden.

Across

1 Cavalryman (6)
4 Fraudulent scheme (4)
7 Furious (3)
10 Jibe (5)
11 Solaced (9)
12 Pigs (4)
13 Container for cut flowers (4)
14 ___ and hearty (4)
16 Commotion (7)
18 Excursion (4)
21 Joke (4)
23 Herb with parsley-like leaves (7)
26 Division of the school year (4)
27 Not at home (4)
28 Support (4)
31 Large fleshy fruit (9)
32 Proverb (5)
33 Primate (3)
34 Traditional board game (4)
35 Beasts (6)

Down

1 Short-handled axes (8)
2 Slothful person (8)
3 Singing voice (4)
5 Remark (7)
6 Debatable (4)
7 "Our ___ Friend" (Dickens novel) (6)
8 Avoided (6)
9 Scribble (6)
15 Go on horseback (4)
17 Sign of things to come (4)
19 Cloudy (8)
20 Indoor footwear (8)
22 Snared (7)
23 Cowardly (6)
24 Imaginary perfect place (6)
25 Alloy of copper and tin (6)
29 Postal service (4)
30 Den (4)

Scented

*When the crossword is completed, the shaded squares will spell out
the name of a popular scented plant.*

Across

1 Popular indoor plant with variegated coloured leaves (6)
4 Mathematical proposition (7)
9 Short work of fiction (9)
10 Vertical part of a stair (5)
11 Concludes (4)
12 Fleet (4)
13 ___ McPherson (supermodel) (4)
15 Completely (7)
17 Vocalist (6)
19 Tantalised, bantered (6)
21 Commenced (7)
24 Rind (4)
25 Fail to include (4)
26 Part of the leg (4)
30 Smell (5)
31 Heavy waterproof cover (9)
32 Wearing clothes (7)
33 Small smooth rounded stone (6)

Down

1 Competition (7)
2 Furious (5)
3 Hybrid citrus fruit (4)
4 Dozens (7)
5 Republic of Ireland (4)
6 Recovering readily from adversity (9)
7 Liverpool's river (6)
8 Mean, ungenerous (6)
14 Expression of woe (4)
16 So (9)
18 Biblical boat builder (4)
20 Reduced in rank (7)
21 One of the planets (6)
22 Protection (7)
23 Sustain (6)
27 Unrehearsed (2,3)
28 Flag (4)
29 Free from danger (4)

Dianthus

When the crossword is completed, the shaded squares will spell out the name of a variety of dianthus.

Across

1   Herb with blue flowers (6)
4   Bandit (7)
9   Lawyer (9)
10 Male birds (5)
11 Variety (4)
12 Type of soil with a low pH value (4)
13 At liberty (4)
15 Bushy clump of grass (7)
17 Shed for aircraft (6)
19 Wanton destroyer (6)
21 Fine yellow cornmeal common in Italy (7)
24 Deeds (4)
25 Boxing match (4)
26 ___ rubrum (red maple) (4)
30 Join together (5)
31 Purpose (9)
32 Beneficiary of a will (7)
33 Pair (6)

Down

1   Look after children (7)
2   More uncommon (5)
3   Hold tight (4)
4   Make bright by rubbing (7)
5   Move by slow degrees (4)
6   Find out (9)
7   Cloth used with polish (6)
8   Assail (6)
14 River crossing (4)
16 Causing momentary shock (9)
18 Invalid, not binding (4)
20 Characteristic of or resembling a lion (7)
21 Small and dainty (6)
22 Organise (7)
23 Free-and-easy (6)
27 Monkey (5)
28 Canvas shelter (4)
29 Loosen (4)

Formal

When the crossword is completed, the shaded squares will spell out the name of a shrub suitable for formal gardens.

Across

1 Bear's ___ (acanthus) (8)
5 Grown-ups (6)
9 Follow as a result (5)
10 Riddle (9)
12 Urban areas (5)
13 Furrows caused by wheels (4)
14 Equitable (4)
16 Autocrat (6)
18 Specimen (7)
21 Overture (7)
23 Jewish language (6)
25 Compass bearing (4)
27 Boast (4)
28 Employees (5)
30 Bones of the spinal column (9)
31 Musical drama (5)
32 Illuminations (6)
33 Vanquished (8)

Down

1 Baby's ___ (gypsophila) (6)
2 In another place (9)
3 Game played on a checkered board (5)
4 Selected passage (7)
6 Have a meal (4)
7 Immature form of insect (5)
8 English county (8)
11 Saltpetre (5)
15 Attire (4)
17 Advantage (4)
19 Widespread (9)
20 Disruption (8)
22 Mistake (5)
23 Science or art of preserving health (7)
24 Frightened (6)
26 Small shoot or twig (5)
28 Glowed (5)
29 Vegetable matter dug from a bog (4)

Shrubbery

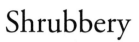

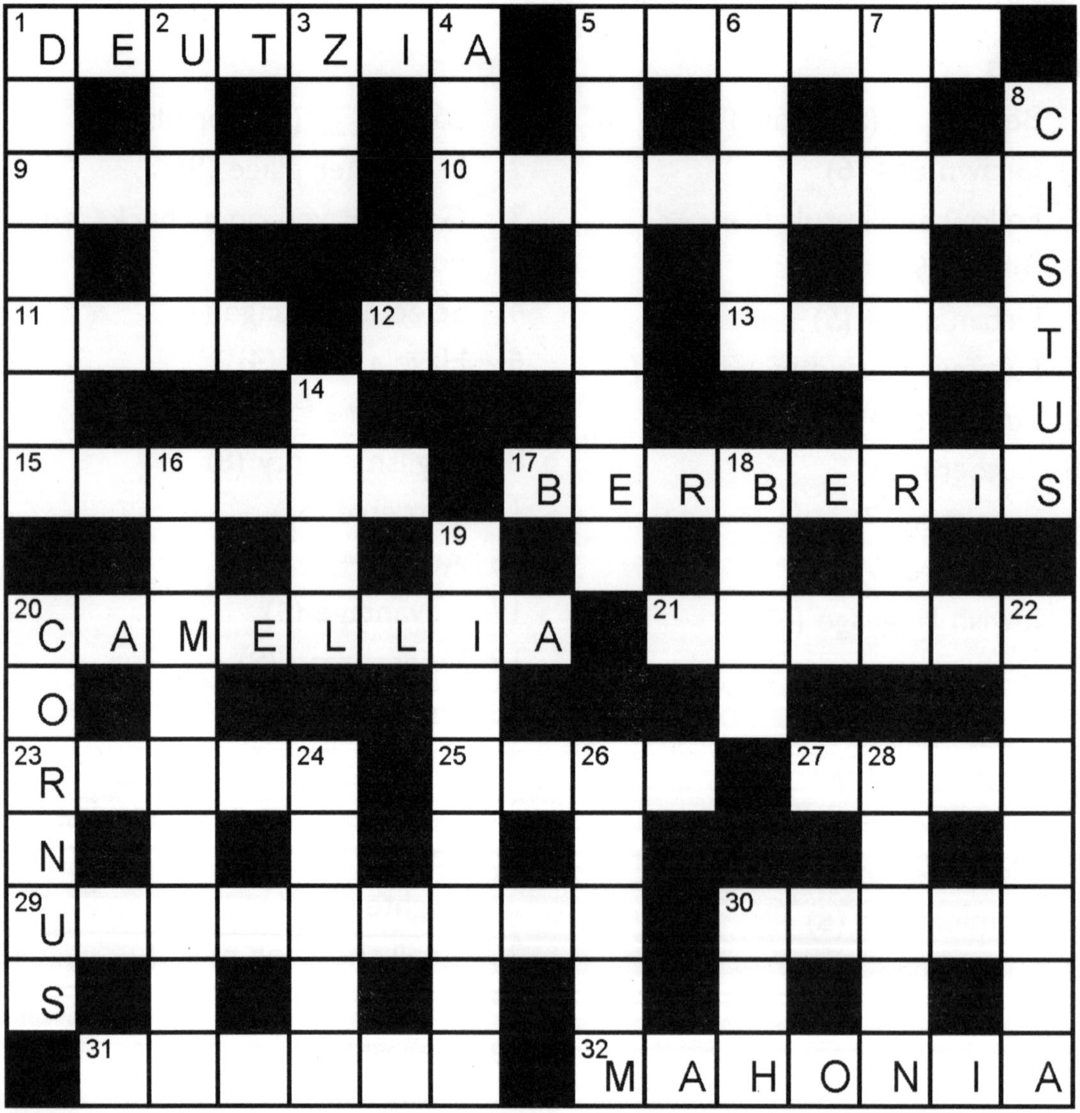
DEUTZIA
CISTUS
BERBERIS
CAMELLIA
CORNUS
MAHONIA

This crossword has been planted with a selection of shrubs.
All you have to do is 'plant' the answers to the remaining clues.

Across

1   SHRUB (7)
5   Sleepy (6)
9   Arrange in line (5)
10 Perfume derived from the dried branches of an Asian shrub (9)
11 Variegated (4)
12 Dry up, scorch (4)
13 Automaton (5)
15 The drink of the gods (6)
17 SHRUB (8)
20 SHRUB (8)
21 Forgive (6)
23 Souvenir (5)
25 Temporary stitch (4)
27 Sicilian volcano (4)
29 Expression in speech (9)
30 Market-place in ancient Greece (5)
31 Loose from moorings (6)
32 SHRUB (7)

Down

1   Showing no expression (7)
2   Merge (5)
3   Japanese branch of Buddhism (3)
4   Fruit tree (5)
5   Shilly-shallied (8)
6   Different (5)
7   Slept (9)
8   SHRUB (6)
14 Small sailing-boat (4)
16 Finished (9)
18 Boast (4)
19 Well-defined (8)
20 SHRUB (6)
22 North American falls (7)
24 Short-legged dog (5)
26 Elite (5)
28 Prickle (5)
30 Fraxinus (3)

Tomato

*When the crossword is completed, the shaded squares will spell out
the name of a variety of tomato.*

Across

1 Well thought of (8)
5 Tender evergreen mimosa with yellow or white flowers (6)
9 Professorship (5)
10 Give a guided tour (4,5)
12 Prose composition (5)
13 Floating platform (4)
14 Ale (4)
16 Firmly established (6)
18 Retort (7)
21 Naval rank (7)
23 Notified of danger (6)
25 ___ and crafts (4)
27 Lacking colour (4)
28 Ethical (5)
30 Waxy variety of potato (9)
31 Pretend (5)
32 Shrub of the Rhododendron genus with showy flowers (6)
33 Sea between Italy and the Balkans (8)

Down

1 Go beyond (6)
2 Change into another shape (9)
3 Before the appointed time (5)
4 Guaranteed (7)
6 Stiff paper (4)
7 Waterfall slide (5)
8 One of the Channel Islands (8)
11 Tender (5)
15 Short flowering or fruit-bearing branch (4)
17 Biblical weed (4)
19 Common garden herb (9)
20 Don Quixote's home (2,6)
22 Smallest (5)
23 Saturday and Sunday (7)
24 Health centre (6)
26 Jewelled headdress (5)
28 Civilian dress (5)
29 Adhesive (4)

Celebrity Gardener

When the crossword is completed, the shaded squares will spell out the name of a celebrity gardener.

Across

1 Skimpy (6)
4 Force (6)
10 Punctuation mark (9)
11 Noblemen (5)
12 The woody stem of a raspberry etc. (4)
13 Computer programs (8)
16 Japanese dish with small cakes of cold rice, fish, etc. (5)
17 African or French marigold (7)
19 Fresh (3)
20 Sardonic (7)
22 Fleshy parts of ears (5)
24 Common weed in lawns (8)
27 Baby carriage (4)
31 Angry (5)
32 Previously unknown (7-2)
33 North American country (6)
34 Cameos (anagram) – summer-flowering annual (6)

Down

1 Harmonious sounds (5)
2 Nuts used to make marzipan (7)
3 Stone (4)
5 Last Greek letter (5)
6 Faultless (7)
7 Mislaid (4)
8 Permitting (8)
9 Tangle (4)
14 Audio equipment (2-2)
15 Egyptian goddess of fertility (4)
16 Not all (4)
17 Dusk (8)
18 Sea bird (4)
21 Army or navy rank (7)
23 Ennui (7)
25 Alter (5)
26 Long shallow basket for carrying flowers and fruit (4)
28 Criminal organisation (5)
29 Bluish-white metal (4)
30 Filled tortilla (4)

Perennial

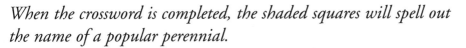

When the crossword is completed, the shaded squares will spell out the name of a popular perennial.

Across

1 Great mob (anagram) – Monarda (8)
5 Coarse printed cotton cloth (6)
9 Neighbourhood pub (5)
10 As a result (9)
12 Brilliant success (5)
13 Notion (4)
14 Capri, for example (4)
16 In front of (6)
18 Most profound (7)
21 Writers (7)
23 Punctual (6)
25 Pound (4)
27 Company emblem or device (4)
28 Not far off (5)
30 Impertinence (9)
31 Automaton (5)
32 Donkey's bray (6)
33 Stubbornly persistent (8)

Down

1 Faith (6)
2 Remember (9)
3 Apportion (5)
4 Not indoors (7)
6 Cain's brother (4)
7 Golf clubs (5)
8 Cooked egg dish (8)
11 Make corrections to (5)
15 Notorious Roman emperor (4)
17 Woodwind instrument (4)
19 Spurge (9)
20 Conquer (8)
22 Exhibited (5)
23 Adage (7)
24 Vessel for boiling water (6)
26 Offspring (5)
28 Greek holiday island (5)
29 ___ Fitzgerald (jazz singer) (4)

Cotswolds

150

When the crossword is completed, the shaded squares will spell out the name of a famous garden in the Cotswolds.

Across

1 Colour of the spectrum (6)
4 Garland or wreath for the head (7)
9 Feeling justifiable anger (9)
10 British soldier (5)
11 ___ mallow (Lavatera) (4)
12 Broad (4)
13 Famous public school (4)
15 Riding a bike (7)
17 Linger, lurk (6)
19 Bold as brass (6)
21 Garden plant with round flat papery silver-white seedpods (7)
24 Naked (4)
25 Stopper (4)
26 Wander (4)
30 Historical memento (5)
31 Puritan (9)
32 Spendthrift (7)
33 Away from the coast (6)

Down

1 Crackbrained (7)
2 Ruse (5)
3 Jokes (4)
4 Fortress (7)
5 Gaming stake (4)
6 Infinite (9)
7 Vexatious (6)
8 Insect with large rear pincers (6)
14 Putting on the ___ (4)
16 Royal disc (anagram) – fumewort (9)
18 Hostelries (4)
20 Impartial (7)
21 Important person (4-2)
22 Conceded (7)
23 Patron saint of Scotland (6)
27 Greek vowel (5)
28 Cliff (4)
29 Supreme Norse deity (4)

Potato

When the crossword is completed, the shaded squares will spell out
the name of a variety of potato.

Across

1 Vegetables associated with Wales (5)
4 Uncertainty (5)
7 Chart (3)
9 Tobacco plant (9)
10 Type of parrot (5)
11 Apiece (4)
13 Golden rod (8)
17 Marine algae (7)
18 Grieved over (7)
20 Protective eyewear (7)
22 Go before (7)
23 Arrogant (anagram) – herb (8)
24 Second Greek letter (4)
28 Capital of Japan (5)
30 Large breed of dog (5,4)
32 Fodder crop (3)
33 Bush (5)
34 Requirements (5)

Down

1 Jousting weapon (5)
2 And the rest (3)
3 Location (4)
4 Precious stone (7)
5 Radioactive element (7)
6 Barbara's husband in "The Good Life" (3)
7 Exaggeratedly masculine (5)
8 Minor chess piece (4)
12 Ailsa ___, popular variety of tomato (5)
14 Entertained (6)
15 Underground room (6)
16 Unused (4)
17 Low-growing perennial shrub whose leaves are used in cooking (4)
19 Female relative (5)
21 Pompous gait (7)
22 Traditional saying (7)
23 Hungarian wine (5)
25 Regions (5)
26 US state settled by Mormons (4)
27 Daze (4)
29 Operations, abbreviated (3)
31 "Cakes and ___" (Somerset Maugham title) (3)

153

Summer Bedding

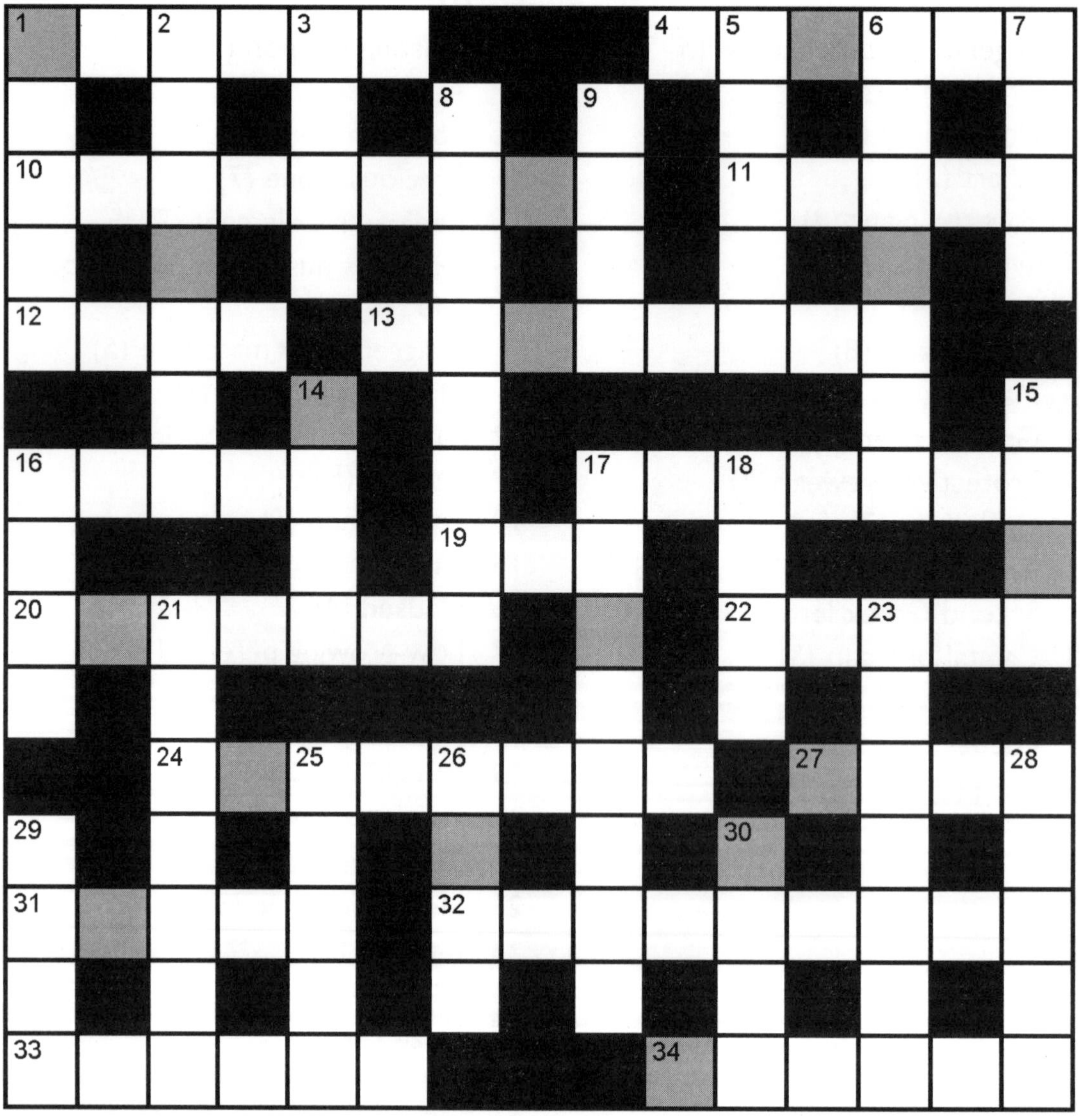

*When the crossword is completed, the shaded squares will spell out
the name of a summer bedding plant.*

Across

1 Centre (6)
4 Pact (6)
10 A variety of green sprouting broccoli (9)
11 Linger (5)
12 Insects that can cause sandy heaps in lawns (4)
13 Places where trees are grown for study (8)
16 Move furtively (5)
17 Brilliant red (7)
19 By way of (3)
20 Wyoming city (7)
22 Spiral (5)
24 Emphasised (8)
27 Concealed ditch used in landscape gardening (2-2)
31 Regretting (5)
32 Roving in quest of plunder (9)
33 Fourscore (6)
34 Skimpy (6)

Down

1 Coffee flavouring (5)
2 Erased (7)
3 Scientists' workplaces (4)
5 Fasten again (5)
6 Letters sent by plane (3,4)
7 Toy that goes up and down on a string (2-2)
8 Bring back (8)
9 Nought (4)
14 Quantity of paper (4)
15 Mythical river of the underworld (4)
16 Solitary (4)
17 French wine (8)
18 Hurt (4)
21 Taking a break (7)
23 Foremost (7)
25 Correct (5)
26 Suburban house (4)
28 Corner (5)
29 Faithful (4)
30 Silent (4)

Geum

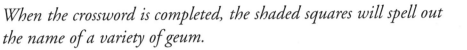

When the crossword is completed, the shaded squares will spell out
the name of a variety of geum.

Across

1 Go by bike (5)
4 Sailor (7)
9 Hypnotism (9)
10 Short (5)
11 Path of a planet (5)
13 Precious metal (4)
14 Bird that can be taught
to speak (4)
16 Coached (7)
18 Pouch worn with a kilt (7)
20 Venetian canal boat (7)
22 Floor-show (7)
24 Peruse (4)
26 — Park, gardens in West
London laid out by Capability
Brown (4)
27 Arab country (5)
28 Electronic sound
reproduction (5)
30 Type of pea (9)
32 Obedient (7)
33 More recent (5)

Down

1 Ease (7)
2 Type of lettuce (3)
3 Vote into office (5)
4 Musk or monkey flower (7)
5 Vein structure in a leaf (3)
6 Loud (5)
7 Abstain (7)
8 Scorched (6)
12 Muscular strength (5)
15 Blunder (4)
17 Corner (4)
19 Less common (5)
20 Floral wreath (7)
21 Very bad (7)
22 ___ grass (Phalaris) (6)
23 Farm vehicle (7)
25 Inspect accounts (5)
27 Demonstrated (5)
29 Lout (3)
31 Small number (3)

Climber

1
2
3
4
5
6
7
8
9
10
11
12
13
14
15
16
17
18
19
20
21
22
23
24
25
26
27
28
29
30
31
32
33

*When the crossword is completed, the shaded squares will spell out
the name of a popular climber.*

Across

1 Recordings (5)
4 Dyed (anagram) (4)
6 Andrew Lloyd Webber musical (4)
10 Curling lock of hair (7)
11 London football team (4,3)
12 Ermine, for example (3)
13 Composer of "The Planets" (5)
14 Fire-raising (5)
15 Crested parrot (8)
18 Commence (5)
20 Given medicine (5)
21 Determined (8)
23 Couple (5)
25 Young eel (5)
28 Flightless bird (3)
29 Submarine weapon (7)
30 Nine iron, in golf (7)
31 Look for (4)
32 Eden occupant (4)
33 Of little weight (5)

Down

1 Frugality (6)
2 Needy (9)
3 Slender graceful female (5)
4 Praise highly (5)
5 Stop work (4,5)
7 Greenfly (5)
8 Creator of Maigret (7)
9 City formerly known as Constantinople (8)
16 Dish made with rice, cooked fish and hard-boiled eggs (8)
17 Triple (9)
19 Assembly (9)
20 Formal discussions (7)
22 Spree (6)
24 See eye to eye (5)
26 Poison (5)
27 Revolt (5)

Parsley

When the crossword is completed, the shaded squares will spell out the name of a variety of parsley.

Across

1 Holiest city of Islam (5)
4 Underground stem producing roots and leafy shoots (7)
9 Gifts (9)
10 Oafs (5)
11 Extol (4)
12 Pod contents (4)
13 Portent (4)
16 Approximately (5)
17 Popular rockery plant (9)
20 Outstanding (9)
22 Hidden store (5)
24 Tarry (4)
26 Squirrel's nest (4)
27 Entreaty (4)
31 Rule (5)
32 Surprising (9)
33 Fortunate (7)
34 Stone carver (5)

Down

1 Pattern (5)
2 Vanquish (7)
3 Opposed (4)
4 Ascends (5)
5 Home for an Eskimo (5)
6 Rich, luxurious (7)
7 Otherwise (4)
8 Put up with (8)
14 Indian dress (4)
15 Overdue (4)
16 Duplicate (4)
18 Incidentally (2,3,3)
19 Strong restless desire (4)
21 Exterior (7)
23 Temperature scale (7)
25 Americans (5)
26 Given medicine (5)
28 Inert gas used in fluorescent tubes (5)
29 Seize (4)
30 Bit of news (4)

Biblical

	1		2			3		4		5		
	6 J	A	C	O	B	7 S	L	A	D	D	E	R	
8												9
10					11							
12			13			14			15			
16 S	T	17 A	R	O	F	18 B	E	T	H	19 L	E	H	E	M 20
21			22			23			24			
25		26			27			28				
		29 S	O	L	O	M	O	N	S	S	E	A	L

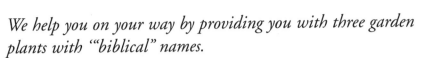

We help you on your way by providing you with three garden plants with "'biblical" names.

Across

6 "BIBLICAL" PLANT (6,6)
10 Lift up (5)
11 Police officer (9)
12 Game played on a lawn (7)
14 Amaze (7)
16 "BIBLICAL" PLANT (4,2,9)
21 Playhouse (7)
23 Hampered (7)
25 Hopeful people (9)
28 Ridges of sand (5)
29 "BIBLICAL" PLANT (8,4)

Down

1 Gambling establishment (6)
2 Tree trunk (4)
3 Go by (4)
4 Period before Christmas (6)
5 Unpleasant child (4)
7 Speedy (5)
8 Autumn ___ (Colchicum) (6)
9 Parched (4)
13 Flying saucer (3)
14 Paintings, sculpture, etc. (3)
15 Expression of distaste (3)
17 Reverential wonder or fear (3)
18 Hive inhabitant (3)
19 Circuit of a race-track (3)
20 Free from pomp or affectation (6)
21 Norse god of thunder (4)
22 Place of worship (6)
23 Norwegian dramatist (5)
24 Concerning teeth (6)
26 Throw carelessly (4)
27 Japanese wrestling (4)
28 Measure of medicine (4)

Bulb

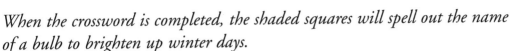

When the crossword is completed, the shaded squares will spell out the name of a bulb to brighten up winter days.

Across

1 Momentary pain (6)
4 Wyoming city (7)
9 Dissimilar (9)
10 No longer fresh (5)
11 Three feet (4)
12 Famous (8)
15 Insectivorous plant, sundew (7)
16 Japanese warrior (7)
18 Very small circular shape (3)
19 Exonerate (7)
21 Newspaper piece (7)
23 Height, elevation (8)
26 Break (4)
30 Mature (5)
31 Everlasting (9)
32 Royal residences (7)
33 Upper part of the windpipe (6)

Down

1 Mixture of spirits, sugar and hot water (5)
2 Conflagration (7)
3 Scottish valley (4)
4 Numbers game (5)
5 Ascended (5)
6 Wander, wind (7)
7 Regular (4)
8 Turncoat (8)
13 Grain ground to powder (4)
14 Small rodents (4)
15 Double (4)
16 Criterion (8)
17 Winged insect (4)
20 Surgeon's knife (7)
22 ___ plant (agave) (7)
24 Pick-me-up (5)
25 Sorts, varieties (5)
27 Versatile garden plant with clusters of usually white, red or purple flowers (5)
28 Pony carriage (4)
29 Wife of Zeus (4)

Plum

166

*When the crossword is completed, the shaded squares will spell out
the name of a variety of plum.*

Across

1   Nitwit (5)
4   God of wine (7)
9   Lawyers (9)
10 Excessive (5)
11 Antelope (7)
13 Bird of prey that feeds on fish (6)
15 Red gem (4)
16 Grassed area (4)
18 Slightly warm (5)
21 Form (5)
22 Wordsworth, for example (4)
24 Theatrical production (4)
25 Imperial measure (6)
27 Pungent red pepper (7)
31 Tropical fruit (5)
32 Victory in a game of chess (9)
34 Mean one (anagram) (7)
35 Confine within bounds (5)

Down

1   Nasal tone (5)
2   Newt (3)
3   Hazard (5)
4   Woodwind instrument (7)
5   Spectrum (anagram) (8)
6   Row of shrubs (5)
7   State of mental agitation (4)
8   Catmint (6)
12 Striped quadruped (5)
14 Jumpy (4)
15 Impetuous (4)
17 Court (3)
19 Structure supporting power cables (5)
20 Prosperous (4-2-2)
22 Brio, flair (7)
23 Surpass (6)
26 "___ Get Your Gun" (musical) (5)
28 Country bumpkin (5)
29 Put up (5)
30 Jane Austen novel (4)
33 Sleeve (3)

Hardy Perennial

When the crossword is completed, the shaded squares will spell out the name of a hardy perennial.

Across

1 Marrow-like plant of the genus Cucurbita (6)
4 Capable of being heard (7)
9 Remember (9)
10 Fries (5)
11 Main part of a church (4)
12 Trader (8)
15 Divide in two (5)
16 Oriental (7)
18 Old measure of 45 inches (3)
19 Deserved (7)
21 Cautious (5)
23 Obstruction (8)
26 Benevolent (4)
30 Out of condition (5)
31 Mostly (2,3,4)
32 Keep in hand (7)
33 High regard (6)

Down

1 Temptress (5)
2 Rude (7)
3 Unaccompanied performance (4)
4 Upper room (5)
5 Capital of Bangladesh (5)
6 Easily broken (7)
7 Comfort (4)
8 Disclosed (8)
13 Gusto (4)
14 Just (4)
15 Church song (4)
16 Extend (8)
17 Bash (4)
20 Snubs (7)
22 Stir up (7)
24 Aquatic mammal (5)
25 Tool for cutting (5)
27 Hard-wearing material (5)
28 Prickly seedcase of certain plants (4)
29 Polynesian garlands of flowers (4)

National Trust

When the crossword is completed, the shaded squares will spell out the name of a National Trust garden.

Across

1 Little angel (6)
4 Competent (7)
9 Required (9)
10 Reasoned thinking (5)
11 Crouch (5)
12 Yorkshire racecourse (9)
14 Recital (anagram) (7)
16 Chic (7)
18 Raising trivial objections (7)
20 Booming bird (7)
22 Cane fruit (9)
24 Weighed down (5)
25 Urge forward (5)
27 Decoration (9)
28 Abandon (7)
29 Stop speaking (4,2)

Down

1 Form of rummy using two decks and four jokers (7)
2 Meet (9)
3 Knock over (5)
4 Pungent red pepper (7)
5 Buddy (3)
6 Prejudiced person (5)
7 Selected passage (7)
8 Wax light (6)
13 Stave off (5)
15 Go up (5)
17 Correction (9)
18 Welsh city (7)
19 Rubbish (7)
20 Enid ___ (children's author) (6)
21 Around-the-clock (7)
23 Excellent (5)
24 Midday meal (5)
26 Meadow (3)

Celebrity Gardener

When the crossword is completed, the shaded squares will spell out the name of a celebrity gardener.

Across

1 Hits with an open hand (5)
4 Abject (9)
9 As easy as ___ (3)
10 Hindrance (3)
11 Offensive sight (7)
12 Inquisitive (4)
13 Long skirt (4)
14 Brazilian dance (5)
16 Awful (8)
18 Use a divining-rod (5)
20 Unpleasant (5)
21 Chronic sleeplessness (8)
22 Flat-bottomed boats (5)
25 Commotion (4)
27 Unobstructed (4)
30 African country (7)
31 Dove-like sound (3)
32 One of the Cinque Ports (3)
33 Vanish (9)
34 Popular Enid Blyton character (5)

Down

1 Beau (5)
2 Forefathers (9)
3 Underwater craft (4)
4 ___ Callas (opera singer) (5)
5 Examples (9)
6 Waterside plants (5)
7 Flower (5)
8 Raise (7)
15 The cry of an ass (4)
17 Sulphur (9)
18 Moist (4)
19 Talked very quietly (9)
20 Settled comfortably (7)
23 Kilns for drying hops or malt (5)
24 Erect, establish (3,2)
26 Become liable for (5)
28 Penurious (5)
29 Shortly (4)

Clematis

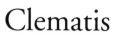

174

When the crossword is completed, the shaded squares will spell out the name of a variety of clematis.

Across

1 Exact copy (7)
5 Brought up (6)
8 Synthetic fabric (5)
9 English county (8)
11 Pile (4)
12 Sweet juicy fruit (4)
13 Further down (5)
15 Proportion (5)
17 Herb (9)
20 Racing dog (9)
23 Hazardous (5)
25 Trust (5)
27 Edges (4)
28 Welsh resort (4)
30 Knitted jacket (8)
31 Trite (5)
32 Tight-fitting undergarment (6)
33 Soothing (7)

Down

1 Cattleman (7)
2 Lively dance (5)
3 Public house (3)
4 Replies (7)
5 Penitence (7)
6 Spring month (5)
7 Alpine plant celebrated in song (9)
10 Gait faster than a walk (4)
14 Winged insect (4)
16 Gilbert and Sullivan opera (3,6)
18 Cooking vessel (3)
19 Not widely distributed (4)
20 Natural talent (4)
21 Honest (7)
22 Devilish (7)
24 Fuel for a Christmas fire (4,3)
26 Skins (5)
29 Indian language (5)
31 Measure of noise intensity (3)

Surrey

When the crossword is completed, the shaded squares will spell out the name of a famous garden in Surrey.

Across

1 Beasts of burden (5)
4 Occidental (7)
9 Army rank (9)
10 Throw (5)
11 Floating platform (4)
12 Nimble (4)
13 Demonstrate (4)
16 ___ lily (Zantedeschia) (5)
17 Act on behalf of (9)
20 Tunnel man (anagram) – abrogation (9)
22 Unwind (5)
24 ___ Sharif (film star) (4)
26 Small brown bird (4)
27 Cultivate (4)
31 Come clean (3,2)
32 Disaster at sea (9)
33 Equilibrium (7)
34 Synthetic fabric (5)

Down

1 Brownish yellow (5)
2 Adept (7)
3 Unwanted e-mail (4)
4 Fret (5)
5 Settees (5)
6 Part of a serial (7)
7 Near (4)
8 Scatter (8)
14 Bucket (4)
15 River of Hades (4)
16 Stuff (4)
18 Pitiable (8)
19 Lord (4)
21 In name only (7)
23 Theft (7)
25 Yorkshire racecourse (5)
26 Squander (5)
28 Rouse (5)
29 Burial place (4)
30 Pitcher (4)

Autumn Colour

When the crossword is completed, the shaded squares will spell out the name of a plant for autumn colour.

Across

1 Flummoxed (7)
5 Rabbit's home (6)
8 Lorry (5)
9 Waxy variety of potato (9)
11 Riotous feast (4)
12 Italy's capital (4)
13 Cook in an oven (5)
15 Plant fibre used for making rope (5)
17 Rum (8)
20 Tolerable (8)
21 In front (5)
24 Child, colloquially (5)
26 Group of people working in combination (4)
27 ___ graveolens, herb of grace (4)
30 Driver (9)
31 Entertain (5)
32 Hate intensely (6)
33 Erudite (7)

Down

1 Cinderella's friend (7)
2 Thrown (5)
3 Be fond of (4)
4 Medical practitioner (6)
5 Item of jewellery (8)
6 Measuring stick (5)
7 Cut off socially (9)
10 Enrol (5)
14 Bone in the forearm (4)
16 Flight of steps (9)
18 US state (4)
19 Use badly (3-5)
20 Fundamental (5)
22 Cul-de-sac (4,3)
23 Cask (6)
25 Blunder (5)
28 Reversal of direction (1-4)
29 Most populous island of Indonesia (4)

Landscape Gardener

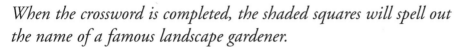

When the crossword is completed, the shaded squares will spell out the name of a famous landscape gardener.

Across

1 Nice shop (anagram) – globe thistle (8)
5 Debacle (6)
9 Labyrinths (5)
10 Sedum (9)
12 Linger (5)
13 Above (4)
14 Whirl (4)
16 Destructive migratory insect (6)
18 Cut of beef (7)
21 Exonerate (7)
23 Spiritlessness (6)
25 Waggish (4)
27 Son of Isaac (4)
28 Precious stone (5)
30 Forsaken (9)
31 Egypt's capital (5)
32 Special aptitude (6)
33 City for sprouts? (8)

Down

1 Antagonism (6)
2 Risky (9)
3 Not nice (5)
4 Faint (4,3)
6 Wild mountain-goat (4)
7 Disrobe (5)
8 Adversary (8)
11 Follows orders (5)
15 Song from an opera (4)
17 Offensive to the sight (4)
19 Alternatively (9)
20 Waterfall (8)
22 Ruhr industrial centre (5)
23 Apart (7)
24 Arm joints (6)
26 Go on all fours (5)
28 Supports (5)
29 1950s prime minister (4)

Dahlias

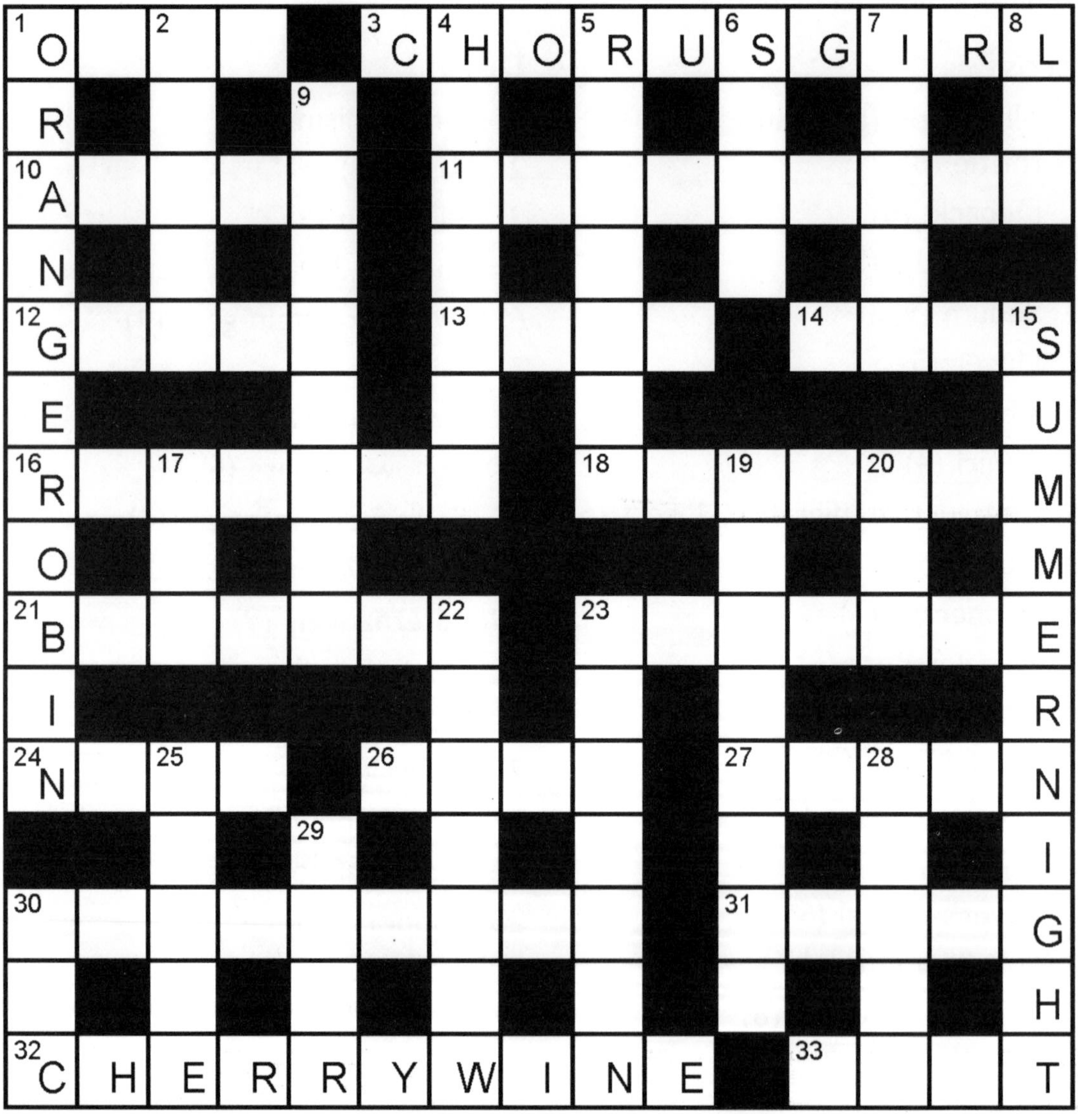
CHORUS GIRL
ORANGE ROBIN
SUMMER NIGHT
CHERRY WINE

We hope you like the four dahlia varieties we have provided
for you in this crossword.

Across

1 Kiln for drying hops or malt (4)
3 DAHLIA (6,4)
10 Horrify (5)
11 Legendary outlaw (5,4)
12 Protect (5)
13 Wicked (4)
14 Egyptian goddess (4)
16 Old soldier (7)
18 Monotonous (7)
21 Making beer (7)
23 Entourage (7)
24 After deductions (4)
26 Wet weather (4)
27 Small crustacean (5)
30 Ticking-off (7-2)
31 Due (5)
32 DAHLIA (6,4)
33 Undershirt (4)

Down

1 DAHLIA (6,5)
2 Brown pigment (5)
4 Most difficult (7)
5 Bosh (7)
6 Male offspring (4)
7 Fetters (5)
8 Conducted (3)
9 Plants of the iris family with brightly coloured flower spikes (8)
15 DAHLIA (6,5)
17 Perish (3)
19 Figure of speech (8)
20 Hasten (3)
22 Scotland's largest city (7)
23 Capital of Burma (7)
25 Fine net fabric (5)
28 Nimble, spry (5)
29 Level, layer (4)
30 Involuntary habitual response (3)

Floribunda

When the crossword is completed, the shaded squares will spell out the name of a variety of floribunda rose.

Across

1 Travel to and from work (7)
5 Prickly plants (6)
9 Artificial silk (5)
10 Young plants (9)
11 Company (4)
12 Food for carnivores (4)
13 Male duck (5)
15 Foliage (6)
17 Young hares (8)
20 Deathless (8)
21 Marine gasteropods (6)
23 Convenient (5)
25 ___ Blyton (children's author) (4)
27 Pace (4)
30 Baltic country (9)
31 Third largest city in Japan (5)
32 Thrifty (6)
33 One of Shakespeare's plays (7)

Down

1 Cautious (7)
2 Civic dignitary (5)
3 Vases (4)
4 Follow as a result (5)
5 Accords (8)
6 Lubricated (5)
7 Peerless example (9)
8 Appraise (6)
14 Ale (4)
16 Type of carpet (9)
18 Repeated sound (4)
19 Motherly (8)
20 Breathe in (6)
22 Female singing voice (7)
24 Youthful (5)
26 US state (5)
28 Lag behind (5)
29 Reluctant (4)

Dogwood

186

*When the crossword is completed, the shaded squares will spell out
the name of a variety of dogwood.*

Across

1   Non-iron (4-3)
5   Cordiality (6)
9   Portion (5)
10 In another place (9)
11 Expel (4)
12 Border (4)
13 More pleasant (5)
15 Existing in fact (6)
17 Wedlock (8)
20 End of the line (8)
21 Piece of sculpture (6)
23 Kingdom (5)
25 Scientists' workplaces (4)
27 Functions (4)
30 Lawyer (9)
31 Dry Spanish wine (5)
32 Innate (6)
33 Freedom (7)

Down

1   Certificate of attainment (7)
2   Concepts (5)
3   Composition for two performers (4)
4   Crop (5)
5   Methodist (8)
6   Mountain ash (5)
7   Forthright (9)
8   Edict (6)
14 Long skirt (4)
16 Strong waterproof sheet (9)
18 Duty list (4)
19 News report (8)
20 Song bird (6)
22 Rapture (7)
24 Exaggeratedly masculine (5)
26 ___ Cook (popular modern artist) (5)
28 Scrub (5)
29 Wild apple (4)

Evergreen Shrub

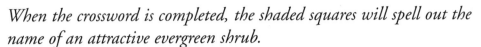

When the crossword is completed, the shaded squares will spell out the name of an attractive evergreen shrub.

Across

1   Own up (7)
5   Peevish (6)
8   Muggy (5)
9   Extend (8)
11 Flowers not yet opened (4)
12 Domesticated (4)
13 Compass (5)
15 Commerce (5)
17 Partner (9)
20 Extremely funny (9)
23 Staple (5)
25 Dresses (5)
27 Second-hand (4)
28 Relocate (4)
30 Out of date (8)
31 Deceit (5)
32 Become less severe (6)
33 Not so old (7)

Down

1   Live together (7)
2   Wanderer (5)
3   Conclusion (3)
4   Dried seedless grape (7)
5   Nuts from a horse chestnut tree (7)
6   Following (5)
7   Plants with a two-year life cycle (9)
10 The Venerable ___ (old historian) (4)
14 Dread (4)
16 Permissible (9)
18 Former French coin of low denomination (3)
19 Young bears (4)
20 Lofty (4)
21 Wealthy, luxuriant (7)
22 Landscape features (7)
24 Cheese (7)
26 Feed a furnace (5)
29 Ape found only in Borneo and Sumatra (5)
31 Common viral infection (3)

Garden Designer

When the crossword is completed, the shaded squares will spell out the name of a famous garden designer.

Across

1 Part of a leg (5)
4 Old Nick (7)
9 Incisive (9)
10 Legal right to ownership (5)
11 Facts given (4)
12 Cruel fairytale giant (4)
13 Enormous (4)
16 Digging tool (5)
17 Able to bounce back (9)
20 Harmful (9)
22 Arrive at (5)
24 Printing fluids (4)
26 Watery part of milk, separated from the curd (4)
27 Number of the Muses (4)
31 Tropical fruit (5)
32 Eminent Greek philosopher (9)
33 Hemerocallis (3,4)
34 Clemency (5)

Down

1 Carried (5)
2 Reluctance to move (7)
3 White Rhine wine (4)
4 Leave undisturbed (3,2)
5 Bag (5)
6 Weariness (7)
7 Tall stiff marsh or water grass (4)
8 Australian marsupial (8)
14 Fruit tree with "Conference" as a popular variety (4)
15 Engrave (4)
16 Slender (4)
18 Of pesticides, spreading through plants to make them toxic to insects (8)
19 Turkish currency (4)
21 Winter month (7)
23 Airman (7)
25 Hindu religious instructor (5)
26 Tired (5)
28 Foe (5)
29 Old (4)
30 Stalk (4)

Perennial

When the crossword is completed, the shaded squares will spell out the name of a delightful perennial.

Across

1 Coax (7)
5 Italian city noted for ham (5)
9 Hangman's halter (5)
10 ___ pear (avocado) (9)
11 Purchases (4)
12 Power or right to reject a proposal (4)
13 Bend down (5)
15 Hand-thrown shell (7)
18 Repeat (7)
20 Less expensive (7)
21 Signified (7)
23 Strength (5)
25 Tidings (4)
27 Theatre gallery (4)
30 Harmless (9)
31 Child (5)
32 Abominable snowmen (5)
33 Bolshy (7)

Down

1 Excessively talkative person (7)
2 Hard dark wood (5)
3 Parliament (4)
4 Rub out (5)
5 Exposed to public scorn (9)
6 Bognor ___ (5)
7 Space traveller (9)
8 Threefold (6)
14 Coarse file (4)
16 Sudden crisis (9)
17 Wrong (9)
19 Sea-eagle (4)
20 Enter (4,2)
22 Wreck (7)
24 Not expressed directly (5)
26 Stinging insects (5)
28 Confess (3,2)
29 ___ Khayyam (4)

Hybrid Tea

When the crossword is completed, the shaded squares will spell out the name of a popular hybrid tea rose.

Across

1 Inimical (7)
5 Smile radiantly (4)
9 Dizzy (5)
10 English county (9)
11 Nought (3)
12 Four roods (4)
13 Tartan cloth (5)
15 Mountain-dwelling antelope (7)
17 Abhorrence (6)
20 Criminals (6)
21 Distinguished (7)
24 State between Oregon and Wyoming (5)
26 Cook in an oven (4)
27 Possessed (3)
29 Uncomfortable (3,2,4)
30 Snow leopard (5)
31 Glance over (4)
32 Lone player (7)

Down

1 Naturally grown (7)
2 Foot-operated lever (5)
3 Largest of Inner Hebrides (4)
4 Dejected (8)
5 More daring (6)
6 Author of many fables (5)
7 Differ (8)
8 Required (6)
14 ___ orange (Philadelphus) (4)
16 Charming, lovely (8)
18 Analogous (4)
19 Devil-may-care (8)
20 Critical situation (6)
22 Neatest (7)
23 Acquire (6)
25 Relating to sight (5)
27 Language in India (5)
28 Implement (4)

A Flower for Winter

When the crossword is completed, the shaded squares will spell out the name of a popular winter-flowering plant.

Across

1   Sea pink (6)
4   Response (8)
10   Copious, abundant (5)
11   Speeded up (9)
12   Couples (4)
13   Bound in gratitude (8)
16   Disproved (7)
17   Acrobat's swing (7)
19   Reddish-purple (7)
22   Infantile (7)
24   Catastrophe (8)
26   Solomon's ___ (Polygonatum) (4)
30   Meddle (9)
31   Lifeless (5)
32   Lack of strength (8)
33   Torment (6)

Down

1   Distinguishing feature (5)
2   Rebuke (7)
3   Bend (4)
5   Daring feat (7)
6   Gave way (5)
7   Acute (7)
8   Naked (4)
9   Decapitate (6)
14   Stupefy (4)
15   Network (4)
16   Hoar-frost (4)
18   Morus ___ (white mulberry) (4)
20   Clarkia (7)
21   Replies (7)
22   Beer producer (6)
23   Type of lettuce (7)
25   Temptress (5)
27   River of forgetfulness (5)
28   Opinion (4)
29   Quarter of a pint (4)

Celebrity Gardener

When the crossword is completed, the shaded squares will spell out the name of a celebrity gardener.

Across

1 Eye make-up (7)
5 Song bird (6)
8 Considerable (5)
9 Kitchen strainer (8)
11 Urban area (4)
12 Wharf (4)
13 Selected as the best (5)
15 Drained of colour (5)
17 Say one is sorry (9)
20 Feeling (9)
23 Cherished desire (5)
25 Young ladies (5)
27 Smallest piglet of a litter (4)
28 Brandy made from grapeskins and other refuse from wine-making (4)
30 Plant whose stems may be candied (8)
31 Distress signal (5)
32 Capsicum (6)
33 Samson's temptress (7)

Down

1 Citizen army (7)
2 Dried stalks (5)
3 Grow older (3)
4 ___ azurea (bugloss) (7)
5 Fox-hunting cry (5-2)
6 Scope (5)
7 Make germ-free (9)
10 Evergreen shrub genus, including the low-growing species pinguifolia (4)
14 Opposed (4)
16 Impediment (9)
18 Play on words (3)
19 Probabilities (4)
20 Long detailed story (4)
21 Sooner (7)
22 Large mug-like vessel (7)
24 Shakespeare play (7)
26 Chimney cleaner (5)
29 Be of use (5)
31 Cornish river (3)

Climbing Rose

When the crossword is completed, the shaded squares will spell out the name of a popular climbing rose.

Across

1 Scatterbrained (5)
4 Drawback (4)
6 Feeling of warmth (4)
10 North African country (7)
11 Jumper (7)
12 Moggy (3)
13 Took legal proceedings (4)
14 Measure down (5)
16 Measure up (8)
19 Old Greek fabulist (5)
21 Arranged for pictorial purposes (5)
22 Nevada city famed for casinos (3,5)
24 Fastening (5)
26 Leap (4)
29 Attempt (3)
31 Crime (7)
32 Abandon hope (7)
33 Compos mentis (4)
34 Coarse fibre from the outer husk of a coconut (4)
35 S. American mountains (5)

Down

1 Quick look (6)
2 Foxglove (9)
3 Spars from which sails are suspended (5)
4 Frighten (5)
5 In addition (4)
7 Tulip (anagram) (3,2)
8 Adoration (7)
9 Tall marsh plant (4,4)
15 A smaller amount (4)
17 Impoverished (8)
18 Deficient in beauty (4)
20 Right side of a ship (9)
21 Large snakes (7)
23 Embellishes (6)
25 Not seriously (2,3)
27 Less than (5)
28 Spaghetti, ravioli, etc. (5)
30 Brief written message, as in an office (4)

A Bunch of Roses

¹A	²L	³L	G	O	⁴L	D	⁵	⁶	⁷	⁸

⁹
¹⁰
¹¹	¹²	¹³	¹⁴
¹⁵C O R N E ¹⁶L I A	¹⁷H A ¹⁸N S A
¹⁹V I R G ²⁰O	²¹D E L I ²²C A T A	²³
²⁴	²⁵	²⁶	²⁷	²⁸
²⁹	³⁰	³¹
³²	³³F E L I C I A

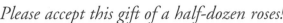

Please accept this gift of a half-dozen roses!

Across

1 ROSE (7)
5 Minor hitches (7)
9 More affluent (9)
10 Come in (5)
11 Doctor's stand-in (5)
13 Upright (5)
14 Path made by animals (3)
15 ROSE (8)
17 ROSE (5)
19 ROSE (5)
21 ROSE (8)
24 Leaf feature (3)
26 The raspberry genus (5)
28 Lowest point (5)
29 Derby venue (5)
30 Name of two US presidents (9)
32 Nuts (7)
33 ROSE (7)

Down

1 To boot (2,4)
2 Meadow (3)
3 Low seat (7)
4 Approach to a house (5)
5 Earth, soil (anagram) – Equisetum (9)
6 Fastest land animal (7)
7 Absolute (5)
8 Lilac (7)
12 Group of singers (5)
16 Brightly spotted beetles (9)
18 Eminent (5)
19 ___ bonariensis, perennial with clusters of tiny mauve flowers (7)
20 Rowers (7)
22 Hide (7)
23 To reap (anagram) – evergreen shrub with large cone-shaped heads of flowers (6)
25 Broom made of twigs (5)
27 Mock (5)
31 And the rest (3)

p4 **Across**: 7 Cheap, 9 Antarctic, 11 Omitted, 12 Moo, 13 Gas, 15 Ali, 16 Nile, 18 Stars, 22 The Garden of Eden, 25 Cheek, 28 Nero, 29 Pea, 31 Red, 33 Tea, 34 Anemone, 36 Buttercup, 37 Spies.
Down: 1 Echo, 2 Gemini, 3 Wand, 4 Arrows, 5 Stag, 6 Ices, 8 Petunia, 10 Tame, 14 Air, 15 Attic, 17 Ludo, 19 Aid, 20 Santa, 21 Knee, 23 Ewe, 24 Flowers, 26 Hoe, 27 Kitten, 29 Profit, 30 Talc, 31 Robe, 32 Date, 34 Alps, 35 Easy.

p6 **Across:** 1 Radio, 4 Ali Baba, 8 Scatter, 9 Plonk, 10 Rued, 11 Leek, 13 Kid, 15 Sister, 17 Twitch, 20 Ton, 21 Stan, 22 Farm, 25 Libra, 28 Release, 29 Shallow, 30 Obeys.
Down: 1 Resorts, 2 Drake, 3 Oath, 4 Agreed, 5 Imp, 6 Ado, 7 Asked, 12 Kiwi, 13 Kit, 14 Bees, 16 Son, 18 Hampers, 19 Harrow, 20 Tills, 23 Awake, 24 Also, 26 Boa, 27 Ail.
ALAN TITCHMARSH – probably the best known gardener in the UK, Alan Titchmarsh has presented Gardeners' World and Ground Force on TV as well as writing several books.

p8 **Across**: 1 Cyclist, 5 Fast, 7 Piano, 8 Yellow, 10 Exit, 11 Forsaken, 13 Butler, 14 Moscow, 17 Sweet pea, 19 Flag, 22 Degree, 23 Dance, 24 Eyes, 25 Trebled.
Down: 1 Copse, 2 Chariot, 3 Iron, 4 Taylor, 5 Full stop, 6 Stock, 9 Snow, 12 Dentures, 13 Boss, 15 Colonel, 16 Repeat, 18 Enemy, 20 Greed, 21 Edge.
SUNFLOWER – or Helianthus. Easy to grow, and growing to over head height, it produces big flower heads in bright yellow which attract bees – and birds for the large seeds.

p10 **Across**: 1 Thyme, 4 Sappers, 8 Examine, 9 Spuds, 10 Both, 11 Scar, 13 Pen, 15 Excite, 17 Knight, 20 Act, 21 Hush, 22 Ewer, 25 Shark, 28 Restore, 29 Stagger, 30 Ingot.
Down: 1 Tremble, 2 Yeast, 3 Erie, 4 Sketch, 5 Pas, 6 Emu, 7 Susan, 12 Rink, 13 Peg, 14 Itch, 16 Cut, 18 Torrent, 19 Usurer, 20 Asses, 23 Wrong, 24 Asti, 26 Ava, 27 Keg.
HAMPTON COURT – the Hampton Court Palace Flower Show is the world's biggest annual gardening event.

p12 **Across**: 1 Calypso, 5 Fear, 7 Tinge, 8 Filthy, 10 Hot, 11 Acre, 12 Asia, 14 Upshot, 15 Fenced, 18 Earl, 20 Lima, 21 Web, 24 Banish, 25 Idler, 26 Omit, 27 Steeple.
Down: 1 Catch, 2 Linctus, 3 Predator, 4 Oxford, 5 Fall, 6 Aphis, 9 Ward, 13 Relative, 14 Used, 16 Cowslip, 17 Lights, 19 Realm, 22 Barge, 23 Gift.
SPIDER PLANT – the spider plant (Chlorophytum) is one of the easiest houseplants to grow. Its colourful foliage is especially effective in hanging basket.

p14 **Across**: 1 Sceptre, 5 Inch, 7 Lapse, 8 Alcove, 10 Dear, 11 Dead ends, 13 Monday, 14 Enmity, 17 Rational, 19 Acid, 22 Earwig, 23 Haste, 24 Tear, 25 Remarks.
Down: 1 Salad, 2 Explain, 3 Tied, 4 Erased, 5 Incident, 6 Coven, 9 I-spy, 12 Man-of-war, 13 Mare, 15 Incisor, 16 Badger, 18 Thame, 20 Dress, 21 Chum.
CHARLIE DIMMOCK – star of Ground Force and other TV gardening programmes.

p16 **Across**: 1 Lettuce, 5 Tubs, 7 Troll, 8 Eye, 9 Lad, 11 Pigs, 12 Heat wave, 14 Attire, 15 Helped, 18 Outstrip, 20 Maze, 23 Aim, 24 Red, 25 Inept, 26 Corn, 27 Primula.
Down: 1 Lit up, 2 Thought, 3 Ugly, 4 Eleven, 5 Treaties, 6 Balsa, 10 Dread, 13 Brethren, 14 Aroma, 16 Plateau, 17 Tied up, 19 Tempo, 21 Extra, 22 Hi-fi.
CHRYSANTHEMUM – one of the most popular garden flowers, may be either annual or perennial, and is available in a vast range of colours.

p18 **Across**: 1 Tramp, 4 Assess, 7 Wee, 8 Teddy, 9 Aft, 11 Shamrock, 13 Stop, 15 Sleuth, 16 Nearly, 19 Rose, 21 Daffodil, 24 Tan, 25 Edges, 27 Ant, 28 Centre, 29 Enter.
Down: 1 Towns, 2 Average, 3 Pet, 4 Addict, 5 Skye, 6 Start, 10 Tipsy, 12 Rats, 14 Deaf, 15 Sprat, 17 Radiant, 18 Dangle, 20 Singe, 22 Later, 23 Kent, 26 See.
RED HOT POKER – or Kniphofia, will grow in any type of garden soil to produce its tall handsome flower spikes

p20 **Across**: 1 Macbeth, 5 Shed, 7 Robin, 8 Nod, 9 Now, 11 Yolk, 12 Espalier, 15 Rarest, 16 Jersey, 19 Stressed, 21 Taut, 24 Sag, 25 All, 26 Erica, 27 Here, 28 Spinach.
Down: 1 Merry, 2 Cobbler, 3 Etna, 4 Honest, 5 Sad, 6 Ennui, 10 Worry, 13 Aces, 14 Asks, 15 Roses, 17 Stamina, 18 Bellis, 20 Rogue, 22 Trash, 23 Semi, 25 Axe.
THE BLACK TULIP – by Alexandre Dumas, is set in 17th century Holland in the period of "Tulipmania" when rare bulbs were bought and sold for incredible sums.

p22 **Across**: 4 Parsley, 5 Mint, 6 Comfrey, 8 Chives, 9 Valerian, 12 Bergamot, 13 Sorrel, 15 Artemisia, 16 Milfoil.
Down: 1 Thyme, 2 Fennel, 3 Rocket, 4 Purslane, 7 Coriander, 8 Chamomile, 10 Marjoram, 11 Betony, 12 Burdock, 14 Basil.

p24 **Across**: 1 Rubbish, 5 Toga, 7 Geese, 8 Popular, 10 Luke, 11 Lent, 13 Sit, 15 Orphan, 16 Orders, 19 Tow, 21 Then, 22 Moss, 25 Narrate, 27 Unite, 28 Chum, 29 Trainer.
Down: 1 Regal, 2 Break up, 3 Ides, 4 Happen, 5 Top, 6 Gales, 9 Rates, 12 Turn, 14 Halt, 15 Often, 17 Emotion, 18 Defect, 20 Worth, 23 Spear, 24 Tuna, 26 Arm.
GROUND FORCE – television's first gardening makeover programme made its debut in 1997 and has been extremely popular ever since.

p26 **Across**: 1 Poser, 4 Sparrow, 8 Gorilla, 9 Santa, 10 Site, 11 Debt, 13 Buy, 15 Sacred, 17 Havana, 20 Rat, 21 Ta-ta, 22 Best, 25 Chest, 28 Natural, 29 Purpose, 30 Worse.
Down: 1 Pegasus, 2 Strut, 3 Roll, 4 Scales, 5 Ads, 6 Run, 7 Weary, 12 Tsar, 13 Baa, 14 Kent, 16 Cut, 18 Astilbe, 19 At once, 20 Recap, 23 Error, 24 Stow, 26 E'er, 27 Two.
POLYANTHUS – this versatile and easily grown perennial comes in a wide variety of colours and is ideal for patio pots and containers as well as beds and borders.

p28 **Across**: 1 Swollen, 5 Decide, 8 Aloha, 9 Milliner, 11 Needled, 13 Goodbye, 15 Dwarf, 17 City, 19 Snap, 21 Bare, 22 Stew, 25 Easel, 27 Codicil, 29 Surpass, 31 Migraine, 33 Vodka, 34 Flying, 35 Nemesia.

Down: 1 Stained, 2 Ozone, 3 Lea, 4 Nomadic, 5 Delight, 6 Chico, 7 Doe, 10 Weep, 12 Lift, 14 Bonus, 16 Acrid, 18 Ice, 20 Year, 21 Back, 23 Tilling, 24 Western, 26 La Scala, 28 Corgi, 30 Andes, 32 Ill, 33 Vim.

WENDY CUSSONS – a classic hybrid tea rose that flowers freely, with highly scented deep pink blooms.

p30 **Across**: 1 Premier, 5 Cosmos, 8 Noise, 9 Sergeant, 11 Integer, 13 October, 15 Excel, 17 Ewes, 19 Give, 21 Roam, 22 Acer, 25 Opera, 27 Pretext, 29 Villain, 31 Sanguine, 33 Daddy, 34 Cornet, 35 Admired.

Down: 1 Pensive, 2 Edict, 3 Ice, 4 Reserve, 5 Corrode, 6 Spent, 7 Own, 10 True, 12 Gale, 14 Bride, 16 Cease, 18 Woe, 20 Roll, 21 Ripe, 23 Catmint, 24 Riviera, 26 Annoyed, 28 Egg on, 30 Adder, 32 Ado, 33 Dim.

ROSE-SCENTED GERANIUM – Pelargonium graveolens, is one of a number of scented geraniums – there are others with lemon, nutmeg or peppermint scented leaves.

p32 **Across**: 1 Longed, 4 Spat, 7 Day, 10 Noble, 11 Leo, 12 Total, 13 Ha-ha, 15 Superior, 19 Forgery, 20 Therapy, 22 Rangoon, 24 Grimace, 25 Indecent, 26 Serf, 30 Riots, 32 Ere, 33 Shoal, 35 Yes, 36 Nest, 37 Tattoo.

Down: 1 Lunch, 2 Nib, 3 Eyed, 5 Protect, 6 Tit, 7 Deter, 8 Yule, 9 Cloudy, 14 Heron, 16 Iberis, 17 Beyond, 18 Type, 19 Fork, 21 Amaze, 23 Nickels, 24 Gander, 25 Irons, 27 Folio, 28 Troy, 29 Asia, 31 Sun, 34 Out.

GRAPE HYACINTH – makes an attractive spring display. The grape hyacinth (or Muscari) usually has blue flowers, but white or pink varieties are available.

p34 **Across**: 1 Swing, 4 Bats, 7 Elf, 10 Atlas, 12 Lay, 13 Yearn, 14 Tom, 15 Romeo, 17 Ops, 18 Fatal, 19 Banquet, 21 Mingled, 23 Charted, 25 All over, 27 Under, 29 Vie, 30 Shrug, 32 Nut, 33 Kylie, 35 Rod, 36 Other, 39 Ere, 40 Then, 41 Midge.

Down: 1 Sea, 2 Ill, 3 Gusto, 5 Alyssum, 6 Sky, 7 Exact, 8 Fondled, 9 Almost, 11 Two, 15 Rob, 16 Manna, 18 Final, 20 Utter, 22 Liver, 23 Chuckle, 24 Diverse, 25 Agenda, 26 Rig, 28 Delve, 30 Storm, 31 Use, 34 Eat, 37 Hid, 38 Roe.

STAR OF BETHLEHEM – the common name of Ornithogalum (also called chincherinchee). Ornithogalums usually have white flowers and are grown from bulbs.

p36 **Across**: I Minaret, 5 Damsel, 8 Dowse, 9 Ill-treat, II Earmark, 13 Matinee, 15 Salon, 17 D-day, 19 Oral, 21 Mite, 22 Glee, 25 Usher, 27 Empower, 29 Debates, 31 King Lear, 33 Eager, 34 Ferret, 35 Decorum.

Down: I Madness, 2 Newer, 3 Rue, 4 Tricked, 5 Dilemma, 6 Merit, 7 Era, 10 Heel, 12 Anne, 14 North, 16 Let-up, 18 Die, 20 Numb, 21 Meek, 23 Largest, 24 Endured, 26 Rostrum, 28 Wager, 30 Tiger, 32 Ike, 33 Etc.

MARSH MARIGOLD – a plant related to the buttercups, produces pure yellow flowers at the end of spring, and is best planted on the edges of a pond.

p38 **Across**: I Get up, 4 Crab, 7 Tic, 10 Style, 12 Oil, 13 Dream, 14 Ass, 15 Taunt, 17 Six, 18 Vodka, 19 Rebound, 21 Decided, 23 Janitor, 25 Sirloin, 27 Paste, 29 Due, 30 Repay, 32 Eye, 33 Thump, 35 Asp, 36 Shoes, 39 Rot, 40 Ages, 41 Satan.

Down: I Gas, 2 Toy, 3 Pleat, 5 Relaxed, 6 Bad, 7 Tread, 8 Command, 9 Tossed, 11 Tea, 15 Tar, 16 Urban, 18 Vicar, 20 Untie, 22 Droop, 23 Jupiter, 24 Red tape, 25 Sleepy, 26 Nay, 28 Squat, 30 Rests, 31 Awe, 34 Pea, 37 Oft, 38 Son.

COTONEASTER – is the most widely used shrub in British gardens. This is not surprising as it provides attractive foliage and berries, and is generally undemanding.

p40 **Across**: I Divan, 4 Kerb, 7 Sap, 10 Optic, 12 Nib, 13 Theft, 14 Hot, 15 Movie, 17 Era, 18 Dunce, 19 Redcoat, 21 Elegant, 23 Heavier, 25 Visible, 27 Union, 29 Try, 30 Hotel, 32 Ate, 33 Hills, 35 Rug, 36 Naked, 39 Yew, 40 Wide, 41 Empty.

Down: I Duo, 2 Vet, 3 Niche, 5 Embrace, 6 Bit, 7 Sheen, 8 Patient, 9 Intent, 11 Pro, 15 Mar, 16 Vodka, 18 Dregs, 20 Onion, 22 Abbot, 23 Haughty, 24 Retired, 25 Voyage, 26 Eel, 28 In-law, 30 Hence, 31 Ewe, 34 Saw, 37 Kip, 38 Dry.

AFRICAN VIOLET – or Saintpaulia, is one of our most popular flowering houseplants.

p42 **Across**: 2 Lettuce, 3 Courgette, 6 Bean, 7 Swede, 8 Cabbage, 10 Beetroot, 12 Capsicum, 14 Carrot, 16 Shallot, 17 Onion, 18 Chicory, 19 Parsnip.

Down: I Squash, 2 Leek, 3 Celeriac, 4 Endive, 5 Kale, 9 Broccoli, 11 Tomato, 13 Celery, 15 Turnip.

p44 **Across**: I Norfolk, 5 Claw, 10 Towed, 11 Tangerine, 12 Beneath, 14 Othello, 16 Stain, 18 Poet, 20 Liar, 23 Luck, 25 Alec, 28 Abyss, 30 Going in, 33 Reduced, 35 Transform, 36 Lamed, 38 Eros, 39 Lexicon.

Down: I Nut, 2 Rowan, 3 Odd, 4 Ketchup, 6 Leech, 7 Whirl, 8 Snooze, 9 Devour, 12 Bus, 13 Aunt, 15 Eel, 17 Arc, 19 One, 21 Ivy, 22 Hard, 23 Lights, 24 Kin, 26 London, 27 Caramel, 29 Sad, 31 Image, 32 Gusto, 34 Comic, 36 Lax, 37 Don.

LABURNUM – its long pendulous sprays of yellow flowers give the laburnum its popular name of golden rain.

p46   **Across**: 1 Fungi, 4 Dray, 6 Maid, 9 Awl, 10 Emend, 11 Value, 12 Canal, 14 Drone, 15 War, 17 Attend, 20 Synonym, 23 Outcast, 25 Almond, 28 Her, 30 Panda, 31 Sense, 33 Fudge, 34 Seine, 35 Ash, 36 Reel, 37 Hang, 38 Dried.

       Down: 1 Fiasco, 2 Nylon, 3 Ideal, 4 Dreaded, 5 Arduous, 7 Allow, 8 Dye, 11 Vietnam, 13 Apt, 16 Ramp, 18 Tot, 19 Example, 21 Nun, 22 Both, 24 Tunisia, 25 Amazing, 26 Ode, 27 Method, 29 Ridge, 31 Steed, 32 Naafi, 33 For.

GRANNY SMITH – derives its name from a real granny Smith – Mrs Maria Smith who first cultivated it in her garden in Sydney, Australia, in the 1860s.

p48   **Across**: 1 Schemed, 5 Spat, 10 Asset, 11 Continual, 12 Feasted, 14 Aerosol, 15 Rouse, 17 Deer, 19 Slim, 22 Seen, 23 Ages, 26 Attic, 28 Uptight, 31 Riposte, 33 Competent, 34 Percy, 36 Deep, 37 Hurry up.

       Down: 1 Sea, 2 Hosta, 3 Mat, 4 Decided, 6 Prior, 7 Truss, 8 Insane, 9 Slalom, 12 Fir, 13 Trek, 16 Use, 18 Eye, 20 Lit, 21 Carp, 22 Source, 24 Gather, 25 Scratch, 27 Cue, 29 Timid, 30 Geese, 32 Sorry, 34 Par, 35 Yap.

CALIFORNIA POPPY – will flower from early summer until the first frosts.

p50   **Across**: 1 Learner, 5 Taxi, 10 Pop up, 11 Carnation, 12 Abysmal, 14 Janitor, 15 Kudos, 17 Sink, 19 Many, 22 Cuba, 23 Asks, 26 Impel, 28 Unearth, 31 Immense, 33 Stonecrop, 34 Havoc, 36 Erse, 37 Rambler.

       Down: 1 Lip, 2 Apply, 3 Nap, 4 Recalls, 6 Again, 7 Idiot, 8 Trojan, 9 Energy, 12 Ark, 13 Moss, 16 Dab, 18 Irk, 20 Amp, 21 Film, 22 Cruise, 24 Sahara, 25 Skipper, 27 Lie, 29 Elope, 30 Reeds, 32 Navel, 34 Hem, 35 Car.

ROY LANCASTER – gardening writer, broadcaster and lecturer. In 1996 he was one of the first recipients of the Institute of Horticulture's Award for Outstanding Service to Horticulture.

p52   **Across**: 1 Shut out, 5 Calf, 10 Cited, 11 Water lily, 12 Dreamer, 14 Dolphin, 15 Droll, 17 Spot, 19 Trot, 22 Pier, 23 Anne, 26 Aloof, 28 Trinket, 31 Prairie, 33 Sotto voce, 34 Grubs, 36 Rely, 37 Saddest.

       Down: 1 Sic, 2 Untie, 3 Odd, 4 Towards, 6 April, 7 Faith, 8 Studio, 9 Cygnet, 12 Dad, 13 Mule, 16 Ore, 18 Pun, 20 Rio, 21 Ta-ta, 22 Potash, 24 Notion, 25 Empress, 27 Fee, 29 Inter, 30 Knoll, 32 Route, 34 God, 35 Sit.

HYDROPONICS – the art or science of growing plants without soil – in beds of sand or gravel through which water containing dissolved nutrients is pumped.

p54   **Across**: 1 Placate, 5 Minim, 9 Roots, 10 Destroyed, 11 Slander, 13 Aintree, 15 Laden, 17 East, 19 Work, 21 Cubs, 22 Diet, 25 Hosta, 27 Enticed, 29 Octagon, 31 Increment, 33 Moses, 34 To let, 35 Rectory.

       Down: 1 Parasol, 2 Aroma, 3 Ads, 4 Endorse, 5 Moron, 6 Nay, 7 Midweek, 8 Essays, 12 Dine, 14 Rooks, 16 Debut, 18 Axe, 20 Chat, 21 Chemist, 23 Indeed, 24 Trotter, 26 Amnesty, 28 Cheat, 30 Gusto, 32 Col, 33 Mac.

LITTLE SWEETHEART – a dwarf sweet pea ideal for borders, containers and patio pots.

p56 **Across**: 1 Belle, 4 Set free, 9 Chamomile, 10 Rigid, 11 Leo, 12 Sofa, 14 Rill, 15 Beef, 19 Three, 20 Calendula, 23 Apiarists, 24 Notes, 25 Mead, 27 Gala, 28 Urge, 31 Eva, 33 Stall, 35 Miserable, 37 Undress, 38 Dowdy.

Down: 1 Backs, 2 Lea, 3 Eton, 4 Smell, 5 Throb, 6 Rug, 7 Eddy, 8 Hibiscus, 13 Furtive, 16 Equator, 17 Tear, 18 Naps, 19 Trap, 21 Listless, 22 None, 26 Delve, 27 Games, 29 Elegy, 30 Esau, 32 Prod, 34 Add, 36 Bow.

LILY OF THE VALLEY or Convallaria majalis – produces spikes of beautiful white bell-shaped flowers in spring.

p58 **Across**: 1 Diocese, 5 Mishap, 8 Sedge, 9 Instance, 11 Abridge, 13 Adhered, 15 Daubs, 17 Tied, 19 Rage, 21 Hail, 22 Boys, 25 Thyme, 27 Longest, 29 Appease, 31 Postpone, 33 Aspen, 34 Remark, 35 Ethical.

Down: 1 Discard, 2 Older, 3 Eve, 4 Evident, 5 Mistake, 6 Stash, 7 Arc, 10 Adze, 12 Dusk, 14 Ready, 16 Union, 18 Icy, 20 Stop, 21 Half, 23 Outlook, 24 Siamese, 26 Eternal, 28 Extra, 30 Aspic, 32 Owe, 33 Ash.

SISSINGHURST – Sissinghurst Castle in Kent has one of the world's most celebrated gardens, the creation of Vita Sackville-West and her husband Sir Harold Nicolson.

p60 **Across**: 1 Egypt, 4 Amateurs, 10 Sandpiper, 11 Rudge, 12 Deutzia, 14 Umpire, 16 Bach, 17 Elbe, 19 Kitty, 22 There, 23 Sows, 25 Once, 26 Influx, 28 Caterer, 32 On cue, 33 Everybody, 35 Scrutiny, 36 Total.

Down: 1 Eased, 2 Yen, 3 Topaz, 5 Marquee, 6 Turnpike, 7 Under, 8 Seek, 9 Sprawl, 13 Uncle, 15 Ryde, 16 Bite, 18 Boo, 20 Tenor, 21 Hellbent, 23 Sixteen, 24 Wicked, 27 Nicer, 29 Tryst, 30 Royal, 31 Dogs, 34 Out.

PAINTED LADY – a variety of runner bean with heavy crops, good flavour and attractive red and white flowers.

p62 **Across**: 1 Astilbe, 5 Cedar, 8 Maple, 9 Oysters, 10 To-do, 12 Tsar, 14 Off, 15 Laurel, 18 Teasel, 21 Bin, 22 Drag, 23 Mows, 27 Replace, 30 Aster, 31 Lilac, 32 Alyssum.

Down: 1 Admit, 2 Tepid, 3 Leek, 4 Egoist, 5 Cos, 6 Due, 7 Restful, 11 Oar, 13 Rue, 14 Ops, 15 Liberal, 16 Urn, 17 End, 19 Arm, 20 Camera, 24 Oaths, 25 Scram, 26 Easy, 28 Pal, 29 Arc.

p64 **Across**: 1 Set up, 4 Abundant, 10 Turquoise, 11 Verdi, 12 New York, 14 Kimono, 16 Meet, 17 Vein, 18 Event, 21 Scent, 22 Boss, 24 Rump, 25 Cubism, 27 Garment, 31 Acute, 32 Keepsakes, 34 Deleting, 35 Nitre.

Down: 1 Satin, 2 Tar, 3 Pluto, 5 Break in, 6 November, 7 Aaron, 8 Trim, 9 Fickle, 13 Where, 15 Step, 16 Mast, 19 Elude, 20 Strident, 22 Bumpkin, 23 Signet, 26 Usual, 28 Risen, 29 Taste, 30 Maid, 33 Kit.

SNOW-IN-SUMMER – the common name of Cerastium tomentosum, whose silvery foliage is covered with thousands of tiny white star-shaped flowers at the end of spring.

p66 **Across:** 1 Totter, 4 Standard, 10 Asplenium, 11 Music, 12 Fizzy, 13 Anon, 14 Iced, 16 Accused, 19 Aroma, 21 Creep, 23 Dryness, 25 Year, 26 Spar, 27 Verdi, 30 Photo, 31 Oversight, 32 Approved, 33 Ballad.

Down: 1 Toadflax, 2 Topaz, 3 Elegy, 5 Tombola, 6 Numb, 7 Associate, 8 Decide, 9 Wizard, 15 Holy, 17 Cock-a-hoop, 18 Skep, 20 Assisted, 22 Papoose, 23 Dorset, 24 Myopia, 27 Vista, 28 Regal, 29 Dodo.

LOLLO ROSSA – an Italian variety of lettuce that has frilly green leaves tipped with red.

p68 **Across:** 1 Yonder, 4 Heathrow, 10 Uncovered, 11 Gouda, 12 Guess, 13 Need, 14 Edit, 16 Squiffy, 19 Spree, 21 Duvet, 23 Ecuador, 25 Torn, 26 Kept, 27 Logic, 30 Ideal, 31 Bone china, 32 Gardener, 33 System.

Down: 1 Youngest, 2 Nacre, 3 Eaves, 5 Endless, 6 Toga, 7 Roundhead, 8 Wealth, 9 Brandy, 15 Urdu, 17 Underwear, 18 Five, 20 Proclaim, 22 Tremble, 23 Extend, 24 String, 27 Lucky, 28 Grist, 29 Flee.

HONEYSUCKLE – one of the most popular climbers as it will thrive in almost any garden.

p70 **Across:** 1 Black, 4 Pips, 6 Oboe, 10 Blunder, 11 Entwine, 12 Eddy, 13 Flea, 14 Pasha, 16 Inedible, 18 Faced, 20 Irene, 21 On the air, 22 Calls, 25 Hack, 27 Sham, 30 Trawler, 31 Redress, 32 Dung, 33 Lyre, 34 Essay.

Down: 1 Bible, 2 Abundance, 3 Kids, 4 Peril, 5 Prevalent, 7 Bliss, 8 Emerald, 9 Stop, 15 Adze, 17 Brotherly, 18 Feel, 19 Caithness, 20 Incited, 23 Learn, 24 Silo, 26 Curve, 28 Messy, 29 Edge.

CORNELIAN CHERRY – Cornus mas – produces attractive golden-yellow flowers in early spring before the leaves appear.

p72 **Across:** 1 Witch, 4 Oath, 6 Talc, 10 Educate, 11 Synonym, 12 Tick, 13 Wade, 14 Wiser, 16 Seedcase, 18 Decay, 20 Fancy, 21 Testator, 22 Unwed, 25 Oust, 27 Pots, 30 Pergola, 31 Rectify, 32 Sash, 33 Stow, 34 Theme.

Down: 1 Wheat, 2 Truncheon, 3 Heal, 4 Opera, 5 Tasteless, 7 Aunts, 8 Comfrey, 9 Gnaw, 15 D-day, 17 Astronaut, 18 Dram, 19 Crocodile, 20 Faux pas, 23 Wares, 24 Dhow, 26 Screw, 28 Style, 29 Scut.

CLAUDE MONET – spent the latter part of his life at Giverny, where he tended his garden and produced many paintings of it. Monet's garden at Giverny today attracts very many visitors.

p74 **Across:** 1 Taste, 4 Adam, 7 Off, 10 Realistic, 11 Clear, 12 Inane, 14 Aim, 15 Miami, 16 Rapidly, 18 Saunter, 20 Placate, 22 Penguin, 24 Aspen, 26 Pan, 27 Ad hoc, 28 Truce, 30 Sometimes, 32 Rid, 33 Rude, 34 Rioja.

Down: 1 Terrier, 2 Spa, 3 Elite, 5 Decamps, 6 Mac, 7 Opera, 8 Farrier, 9 Steady, 13 Alpha, 15 Mourn, 17 Drawn, 19 Tough, 20 Platter, 21 Exposed, 22 Panama, 23 Nicosia, 25 Pound, 27 Alter, 29 Err, 31 Mao.

ARROWHEAD – Sagittaria – a pond plant with leaves shaped like the points of arrows, and mainly white flowers growing above the water on sturdy stems.

p76 **Across**: I Agenda, 4 Unhappy, 9 Mystified, 10 Parka, 11 Named, 12 Lied, 13 Toil, 15 Sailors, 18 Scion, 20 Inept, 22 Scholar, 24 Over, 25 Tutu, 26 Sable, 29 Wrath, 30 Pigheaded, 31 Bayonet, 32 Speedy.

Down: I Admonish, 2 Epsom, 3 Dried, 4 Undress, 5 Hops, 6 Personnel, 7 Yearly, 8 Aisles, 14 Rich, 16 Itinerary, 17 Obey, 19 Friendly, 21 Trumpet, 22 Spurge, 23 Cobweb, 26 Sheep, 27 Budge, 28 Shin.

PYRACANTHA – or firethorn – an attractive shrub with white flowers, red berries – and formidable thorns.

p78 **Across**: I Piccolo, 5 Babies, 8 Still, 9 Alligator, 11 Week, 12 Coin, 13 Tired, 15 Robin, 17 Keepsake, 20 Previous, 21 Run-up, 24 Rakes, 26 Cuts, 27 Fair, 30 Starboard, 31 Miami, 32 Statue, 33 Ottoman.

Down: I Postwar, 2 Chile, 3 Oils, 4 Orator, 5 Balanced, 6 Bigot, 7 Entertain, 10 Ridge, 14 Anti, 16 Breakfast, 18 Park, 19 Purchase, 20 Paris, 22 Persian, 23 Studio, 25 Sabot, 28 Alarm, 29 Omit.

BLACK PARROT – a parrot tulip (with fringed ends to the petals). Not exactly black, but rather a deep burgundy colour.

p80 **Across**: I Helps, 4 Chapter, 9 down under, 10 Vapid, 11 Ellipse, 13 Oscars, 15 Loch, 16 Stan, 17 Trite, 20 Actor, 21 Nook, 23 Pair, 24 Canals, 26 Dungeon, 30 Staff, 31 Irascible, 33 Settler, 34 Soggy.

Down: I Hedge, 2 Law, 3 Slump, 4 Cartoon, 5 Advocate, 6 Taper, 7 Rude, 8 Advent, 12 Licit, 14 Deer, 15 Loam, 18 Inane, 19 Dreadful, 21 Nastier, 22 Ordeal, 25 Apart, 27 Nicks, 28 Needy, 29 Uses, 32 Big.

PENTLAND DELL – a popular potato variety. One of its advantages is that it is resistant to slug damage!

p82 **Across**: I Mimic, 4 Race, 6 Bats, 10 Nectarine, 11 Alter, 12 Damson, 13 Somehow, 17 Oppose, 19 Purchase, 20 Self-heal, 22 Letter, 24 Bayonet, 26 Cherry, 29 Rifle, 31 Greengage, 32 Yank, 33 Stir, 34 Let up.

Down: I Menu, 2 Mecca, 3 Chassis, 4 Reign, 5 Chess, 7 Apt, 8 Strawberry, 9 Tarmac, 14 Heart, 15 Gooseberry, 16 Apple, 18 Pally, 21 Hinder, 23 Eternal, 25 Tight, 26 Clear, 27 React, 28 Keep, 30 Fun.

p84 **Across**: I Trash, 4 Scramble, 10 Incorrect, 11 Talon, 12 Flannel, 14 Annual, 16 Crib, 17 Once, 18 Saved, 21 Touch, 22 Boer, 24 Tins, 25 Guinea, 27 Variety, 31 Basil, 32 Barometer, 34 Extended, 35 Yarns.

Down: I Thief, 2 ABC, 3 Heron, 5 Cottage, 6 Astonish, 7 Balsa, 8 Erne, 9 Merlin, 13 Adieu, 15 Odes, 16 Cats, 19 Voice, 20 Shanklin, 22 Bramble, 23 Elvers, 26 Upset, 28 Rummy, 29 Ypres, 30 Able, 33 Tor.

CORNUS ALBA – dogwood – provides winter colour with its bright red stems.

p86 **Across:** 1 Halve, 4 Suitcase, 10 Legislate, 11 Ember, 12 Year dot, 14 Enamel, 16 Dahl, 17 Ness, 19 Essex, 22 Basil, 23 Dyed, 25 Last, 26 Burden, 28 Hurry up, 32 Taboo, 33 Uncovered, 35 Gentians, 36 Nippy.

Down: 1 Holly, 2 Log, 3 Eased, 5 Useless, 6 Teenager, 7 Amble, 8 Euro, 9 Cattle, 13 Aches, 15 Exit, 16 Debt, 18 Spy, 20 Scary, 21 Gladioli, 23 Don Juan, 24 Ethics, 27 Urban, 29 Raven, 30 Paddy, 31 Stag, 34 Rap.

VILLE DE LYON – a hardy clematis bearing large carmine-red flowers with golden stamens.

p88 **Across:** 1 Ipomoea, 5 Midday, 8 Feign, 9 Confessed, 11 Open, 12 Grit, 13 Loser, 15 Trace, 17 Heat wave, 20 Perspire, 21 Get up, 24 Avens, 26 Cool, 27 Abut, 30 Laborious, 31 Again, 32 Beasts, 33 Nosegay.

Down: 1 In front, 2 Olive, 3 Owns, 4 Accord, 5 Minstrel, 6 Dwell, 7 Assistant, 10 Dirge, 14 Jeep, 16 Agreeable, 18 Togo, 19 Precious, 20 Pearl, 22 Potency, 23 Poison, 25 Sorts, 28 Bragg, 29 Lass.

PIERIS JAPONICA – a beautiful evergreen shrub with long drooping clusters of white flowers. The young leaves are initially a glorious coppery red.

p90 **Across:** 1 Loire, 4 Task, 6 Shad, 10 Scandal, 11 Chutney, 12 Sire, 13 Chic, 14 Heavy, 16 Waterloo, 18 Rigid, 20 Dosed, 21 Beholden, 22 Caste, 25 Real, 27 Hart, 30 Brought, 31 Calming, 32 Lake, 33 Edit, 34 Dwelt.

Down: 1 Lasts, 2 In arrears, 3 Ends, 4 Tilth, 5 Sackcloth, 7 Henna, 8 Dry-eyed, 9 Rush, 15 Feed, 17 Liberated, 18 Rile, 19 Grenadine, 20 Decibel, 23 Smock, 24 Eggs, 26 Ascot, 28 Tight, 29 Clad.

RACHEL DE THAME – gardening writer and broadcaster, appearing on Gardeners' World and other TV programmes. She trained as a dancer with the Royal Ballet before turning to gardening.

p92 **Across:** 1 Towel, 4 Sure, 6 Odes, 10 Ipomoea, 11 Launder, 12 Lies, 13 Riot, 14 Tie up, 15 Perfumed, 18 Aptly, 20 Cello, 21 Immature, 23 Elope, 25 Hoax, 26 Pile, 29 Proverb, 30 Instant, 31 Rare, 32 Stag, 33 Stein.

Down: 1 Twirl, 2 Wholemeal, 3 Loom, 4 Stadium, 5 Related, 7 Dodge, 8 Stroppy, 9 Subtract, 16 Flowered, 17 Elm, 19 Terminate, 20 Cheaper, 21 Inhabit, 22 Meaning, 24 Odour, 27 Eaten, 28 Uses.

UMBRELLA PLANT – or Peltiphyllum – has pink flowers in spring. In autumn the leaves turn a brilliant red.

p94 **Across:** 1 Earth, 4 Rite, 6 Plot, 10 Gallant, 11 Trident, 12 Tact, 13 Soda, 14 Fence, 16 Bastille, 18 Pepys, 20 Tutor, 21 Guernsey, 22 Ebony, 25 Sash, 27 Ecru, 30 Vanilla, 31 Italics, 32 Suez, 33 Zeus, 34 Sight.

Down: 1 Eight, 2 Reluctant, 3 Heat, 4 Ratio, 5 Tete-a-tete, 7 Lie in, 8 Tatters, 9 Tiff, 15 Star, 17 Legislate, 18 Pony, 19 Preaching, 20 Twelves, 23 Ounce, 24 Yell, 26 Swiss, 28 Upset, 29 Ways.

TENNESSEE WALTZ – an upright free-flowering variety of fuchsia with semi-double flowers.

p96 **Across:** 1 Shake, 4 Opposed, 9 Garlanded, 10 Thief, 11 Expel, 13 Tea, 14 Magic, 15 Thyroid, 17 Digress, 19 Enemies, 21 Matthew, 23 Tomes, 25 Rim, 26 Eerie, 27 Nelly, 29 Marmalade, 31 Tyranny, 32 Tweed.

Down: 1 Suggest, 2 Air, 3 E-mail, 4 Old hand, 5 Pot, 6 Swing, 7 Defects, 8 Edited, 12 Payee, 14 Might, 16 Omits, 18 Ether, 19 Extinct, 20 Scrumpy, 21 Memory, 22 Weekend, 24 Miler, 26 Exact, 28 Yen, 30 Ape.

HELIANTHEMUM — or rock rose — an ideal plant for carpeting rockeries or dry slopes.

p98 **Across:** 1 Weave, 4 Edam, 6 Ring, 10 Inhabit, 11 Teenage, 12 Tarn, 13 Plan, 14 Kayak, 16 Decrepit, 18 Bacon, 20 Acted, 21 Talisman, 22 Cells, 25 Oily, 27 Perm, 30 Harbour, 31 Augment, 32 Ling, 33 Mist, 34 Eased.

Down: 1 Whist, 2 Abhorrent, 3 Elbe, 4 Extol, 5 Antenatal, 7 Italy, 8 Gherkin, 9 Peak, 15 Brad, 17 Potpourri, 18 Bass, 19 Ceaseless, 20 Alcohol, 23 Loren, 24 Slow, 26 Least, 28 Muted, 29 Ogle.

VERBASCUM — or mullein — comes in a number of forms, either biennial or perennial.

p100 **Across:** 1 Patella, 5 Tartar, 8 Opium, 9 Anchorite, 11 Eels, 12 Pint, 13 Sited, 15 Youth, 17 Creditor, 20 Bedstraw, 21 Dwell, 24 Rural, 26 Moat, 27 Garb, 30 Heartless, 31 Erica, 32 Edgers, 33 Wrongly.

Down: 1 Progeny, 2 Trial, 3 Lime, 4 Acacia, 5 Taciturn, 6 Rooms, 7 Aristotle, 10 Eider, 14 Chat, 16 Underhand, 18 Dodo, 19 Calmness, 20 Berth, 22 Library, 23 Warsaw, 25 Lithe, 28 Aging, 29 Zero.

LANGPORT WREN — a bearded iris with beautiful rich burgundy flowers.

p102 **Across:** 1 Boasted, 5 Stem, 10 Daisy, 11 Blackbird, 12 Blue tit, 14 Dryness, 16 Robin, 18 Dane, 20 Wren, 23 Alga, 25 Boar, 28 Lemon, 30 Declare, 33 Sparrow, 35 Chaffinch, 36 Order, 38 Gull, 39 Pilgrim.

Down: 1 Bed, 2 Adieu, 3 Try, 4 Debated, 6 Tokay, 7 Maize, 8 Warden, 9 Odds-on, 12 Bar, 13 Tiny, 15 New, 17 Beg, 19 A la, 21 Rum, 22 Elba, 23 Abduct, 24 All, 26 Oceans, 27 Rosehip, 29 Now, 31 Clang, 32 Awful, 34 Rider, 36 Oil, 37 Ram.

p104 **Across:** 1 Epigram, 5 Pirate, 8 Radio, 9 Get across, 11 Taxi, 12 Stir, 13 Rebel, 15 Cache, 17 Bassinet, 20 Larkspur, 21 At sea, 24 Lasts, 26 Erin, 27 Maid, 30 Campanile, 31 Psalm, 32 Ostler, 33 Pattern.

Down: 1 Erratic, 2 Index, 3 Rood, 4 Mighty, 5 Paternal, 6 Recur, 7 Trombones, 10 Split, 14 Bets, 16 Christmas, 18 Soak, 19 Superior, 20 Lilac, 22 Abdomen, 23 Give up, 25 Shawl, 28 Agate, 29 Spit.

MISS BATEMAN — an ideal clematis for a north-facing wall. The flowers have milky white petals with burgundy-tipped anthers in the middle.

213

p106 **Across:** 1 Scale, 4 Chastise, 10 Daredevil, 11 Baker, 12 Matador, 14 Blonde, 16 Mean, 17 Loot, 18 Nacre, 21 Issue, 22 Pith, 24 Arms, 25 Serena, 27 Mingled, 31 Extol, 32 Tolerable, 34 Flamenco, 35 Heads.

Down: 1 Sedum, 2 Air, 3 Ended, 5 Halibut, 6 Subpoena, 7 Irked, 8 Eire, 9 Overdo, 13 Tears, 15 Less, 16 Mail, 19 Coral, 20 Reveille, 22 Plastic, 23 Tumult, 26 Extra, 28 North, 29 Diets, 30 Deaf, 33 Baa.

CAPE MARIGOLD – Osteospermum – opens its flowers only in full sun, and closes them as soon as a cloud appears.

p108 **Across:** 1 Showy, 4 Aromatic, 10 Reluctant, 11 Ogres, 12 Bolster, 14 Rhodes, 16 Dirk, 17 Onus, 18 Infer, 21 Flair, 22 Buck, 24 Crow, 25 Saturn, 27 Improve, 31 Epoch, 32 Aubergine, 34 Finished, 35 Hands.

Down: 1 Scrub, 2 Owl, 3 Yacht, 5 Returns, 6 Myosotis, 7 Terse, 8 Cosy, 9 Barren, 13 Larva, 15 Brow, 16 Daft, 19 Forgo, 20 Draughts, 22 Bondage, 23 Climbs, 26 Adorn, 28 Perch, 29 Epees, 30 Beef, 33 Ion.

MUSSELBURGH – a popular mid-season variety of leek.

p110 **Across:** 1 Repel, 4 Mustang, 9 Ballpoint, 10 Loser, 11 Smile on, 13 Hither, 15 Call, 16 Mars, 18 Range, 21 Rumba, 22 Gold, 24 Nous, 25 Sorbet, 27 Swahili, 31 Infer, 32 Well-known, 34 Tersely, 35 Wider.

Down: 1 Rebus, 2 Pal, 3 Lapse, 4 Matches, 5 Solitary, 6 Aisle, 7 Girl, 8 Vienna, 12 Islam, 14 Lens, 15 Core, 17 Rio, 19 Naomi, 20 Jamboree, 22 Getaway, 23 Lastly, 26 Offer, 28 Askew, 29 Inner, 30 Lift, 33 Old.

MALLING JEWEL – a reliable heavy cropper producing medium to large sweet dark red berries.

p112 **Across:** 1 Order, 4 Salt, 6 Deaf, 10 Cyclone, 11 Stilton, 12 Rose, 13 Idea, 14 Guava, 15 Bulgaria, 18 Nerve, 20 Adder, 21 Appraise, 23 Teach, 25 Oral, 26 Abet, 29 Madeira, 30 Theorem, 31 Tory, 32 Poem, 33 Dryad.

Down: 1 Oscar, 2 Dachshund, 3 Root, 4 Slender, 5 La Scala, 7 Extra, 8 Fanfare, 9 Virginia, 16 Gershwin, 17 Imp, 19 Raspberry, 20 Attempt, 21 Avocado, 22 Phantom, 24 Alder, 27 Timid, 28 Heed.

STOURHEAD – splendid National Trust garden in Wiltshire – an outstanding example of the English landscape style, it was constructed between 1741 and 1780.

p114 **Across:** 1 Ideas, 4 John, 6 Gash, 9 Cistern, 10 Stamina, 12 Mace, 13 Thai, 14 Rings, 16 Parasite, 18 Duchy, 20 Cargo, 21 Vocalist, 23 Macaw, 25 Rise, 27 Fish, 29 Embargo, 30 Entered, 31 Ever, 32 Isle, 33 Midas.

Down: 1 Income, 2 Easy chair, 3 Shed, 4 Jonah, 5 Hostile, 7 Alien, 8 Hearsay, 11 Airedale, 15 Man-of-war, 17 Too, 19 Cashiered, 20 Compere, 21 Various, 22 Shades, 24 Cable, 26 Swede, 28 Item.

AMELANCHIER – known as Juneberry, Serviceberry or Shadbush – has attractive and colourful foliage, blossom and berries at various times of the year.

p116 **Across:** 1 Plateau, 5 Coshed, 8 Pluck, 9 Bindweed, 11 Ruth, 12 Fake, 13 Retie, 15 Spice, 17 Donations, 19 Blameless, 22 Besom, 24 Locum, 26 Rood, 27 Amid, 29 Abundant, 30 Bulge, 31 Remark, 32 Denmark.

Down: 1 Papyrus, 2 Adult, 3 Elk, 4 Upbraid, 5 Canteen, 6 Sewer, 7 Electrons, 10 Zeus, 14 Sere, 16 Irascible, 18 Tuba, 19 Bald, 20 Earmark, 21 Spotted, 23 Midweek, 25 Mensa, 28 Malta, 30 Ban.

ACER PALMATUM – one of the best species for growing as a bonsai tree, it is very ornamental with brilliant red and gold autumn foliage.

p118 **Across:** 1 Prone, 4 Clear-cut, 10 Abundance, 11 Dirty, 12 Hits, 13 Owls, 14 Drag, 17 Snail, 18 Affluence, 21 Imbroglio, 23 Novel, 25 Ages, 27 Foil, 28 Kris, 32 Audit, 33 Lollipops, 34 Endanger, 35 Metal.

Down: 1 Peach, 2 Opuntia, 3 Ends, 5 Leeds, 6 Aided, 7 Certain, 8 Toys, 9 Snowball, 15 Alto, 16 Nell, 17 Slip, 19 Flotilla, 20 Ulna, 22 Baghdad, 24 Vermont, 26 Satin, 27 False, 29 Sisal, 30 Cape, 31 Siam.

CUTHBERTSON – a popular early-flowering variety.

p120 **Across:** 1 French, 4 Splendid, 10 Ailanthus, 11 Glade, 12 Title, 13 Evil, 14 Shoe, 16 Replete, 19 Erode, 21 Ruing, 23 Spouses, 25 Lava, 26 Iran, 27 Taboo, 30 Chase, 31 Fortnight, 32 Disaster, 33 Roused.

Down: 1 Fracture, 2 Eclat, 3 Canoe, 5 Pastime, 6 Edgy, 7 Deathless, 8 Diesel, 9 Cheese, 15 Polo, 17 Peruvians, 18 Exit, 20 Assorted, 22 Giraffe, 23 Sentry, 24 Placid, 27 Tango, 28 Bogus, 29 Hens.

LITTLE SPARTA – the garden of poet Ian Hamilton Finlay in the Pentland Hills south of Edinburgh is a garden composed as a work of art.

p122 **Across:** 1 Violet, 4 Cancel, 10 Personnel, 11 Rural, 12 Rams, 13 Rosemary, 16 Pansy, 17 Retinue, 19 Ire, 20 Chimera, 22 Daisy, 24 Hyacinth, 27 Ache, 31 Rolls, 32 Novelists, 33 Sadder, 34 Laurel.

Down: 1 Viper, 2 Oarsman, 3 Eros, 5 Aorta, 6 Carry on, 7 Lily, 8 Insomnia, 9 Blue, 14 Type, 15 Very, 16 Pick, 17 Relative, 18 Tidy, 21 Inhaled, 23 Incisor, 25 Aisle, 26 Inns, 28 Easel, 29 Iris, 30 Plea.

p124 **Across**: I Depth, 4 Lark, 6 Mass, 10 Con, 11 Mimic, 12 Erode, 13 Shiver, 14 Spiteful, 16 Persia, 17 Contain, 20 Rashers, 22 Rising, 24 Attorney, 27 Absurd, 30 Homer, 31 Upper, 32 Cot, 33 Date, 34 Star, 35 Sadly.

Down: I Ducks, 2 Penniless, 3 Hampers, 4 Limb, 5 Recap, 7 Aloof, 8 Seedling, 9 Beaten, 15 Fats, 17 Card, 18 Announced, 19 Preached, 21 Errors, 23 Suburbs, 25 Tempt, 26 Erupt, 28 Ditty, 29 Spur.

TENDER AND TRUE – a reliable cropper with good flavour.

p126 **Across**: I Possess, 5 Awls, 10 Plonk, 11 Annulment, 12 Basmati, 14 Bizarre, 16 Gaffe, 18 Lied, 20 Palm, 23 Plum, 25 Wake, 28 Waifs, 30 Overdue, 33 Algebra, 35 Paramount, 36 Admit, 38 Dent, 39 Clarify.

Down: I Pop, 2 Shows, 3 Elk, 4 Spaniel, 6 Waltz, 7 Smear, 8 Enable, 9 Stream, 12 Bug, 13 Ares, 15 Asp, 17 Flu, 19 Ink, 21 Ali, 22 Twig, 23 Prompt, 24 Mar, 26 Avenue, 27 Elastic, 29 Spa, 31 Erred, 32 Demon, 34 Bambi, 36 A la, 37 Try.

SPURGE LAUREL – an evergreen shrub, up to one metre tall, with glossy leathery leaves and honey-scented yellowy-green flowers.

p128 **Across**: I Nonstop, 5 Arrow, 9 Sigma, 10 Aquilegia, 11 Retsina, 13 Torment, 15 Meets, 17 Earn, 19 Busy, 21 Bade, 22 Shop, 25 Aspic, 27 Cordial, 29 Scandal, 31 Campanula, 33 Liner, 34 Eagle, 35 Everest.

Down: I Nostrum, 2 Night, 3 Tea, 4 Placate, 5 Abler, 6 Rag, 7 Wealthy, 8 Guitar, 12 Inst, 14 Equip, 16 Elder, 18 Ado, 20 Lava, 21 Bicycle, 23 Helium, 24 Passage, 26 Culprit, 28 Image, 30 Dense, 32 Mug, 33 Lye.

ORIENTAL POPPY – a hardy border plant, originally red but now available in a range of colours.

p130 **Across**: I Moser, 4 Ruby, 6 Club, 10 Leotard, 11 Ammonia, 12 Rake, 13 Jove, 14 Demon, 16 Software, 18 Rowdy, 20 Cumin, 21 Bastille, 22 Mufti, 25 Imam, 27 Skip, 30 Retreat, 31 Onerous, 32 Cent, 33 Nape, 34 Tense.

Down: I Molar, 2 Stockholm, 3 Ream, 4 Rodeo, 5 Blameless, 7 Linum, 8 Blarney, 9 Amid, 15 Stun, 17 Aubrietia, 18 Ruin, 19 Well-known, 20 Cambric, 23 Fit in, 24 Ilex, 26 Atone, 28 Paste, 29 Beet.

LEVELLER – a very popular variety, producing some of the tastiest fruits of all gooseberries.

p132 **Across**: I Prophet, 5 Catkin, 8 Often, 9 Kangaroos, 11 Purloin, 12 Unarmed, 14 Rinse, 16 Serf, 18 Form, 20 Sloe, 21 Trek, 24 Point, 26 Answers, 28 Nairobi, 30 Dedicated, 32 Inert, 33 Apollo, 34 Migrate.

Down: I Prosper, 2 Outer, 3 Hangover, 4 Takings, 5 Conquer, 6 Tiara, 7 I do, 10 Sedum, 13 Maori, 15 Nooks, 17 Eve, 19 Uprising, 20 Scald, 22 Risotto, 23 Kingdom, 25 Thistle, 27 Excel, 29 Omega, 31 Dip.

PASQUE FLOWER – Pulsatilla vulgars – flowers around Easter time, hence the common name pasque-flower, pasque meaning "of Easter".

p134 **Across**: 1 Hussar, 4 Scam, 7 Mad, 10 Taunt, 11 Comforted, 12 Hogs, 13 Vase, 14 Hale, 16 Turmoil, 18 Trip, 21 Jest, 23 Chervil, 26 Term, 27 Away, 28 Prop, 31 Pineapple, 32 Adage, 33 Ape, 34 Ludo, 35 Brutes.

Down: 1 Hatchets, 2 Sluggard, 3 Alto, 5 Comment, 6 Moot, 7 Mutual, 8 Dodged, 9 Scrawl, 15 Ride, 17 Omen, 19 Overcast, 20 Slippers, 22 Trapped, 23 Craven, 24 Utopia, 25 Bronze, 29 Mail, 30 Lair.

LEVENS HALL – the Topiary Garden at Levens Hall in the Lake District is world-famous – the design being basically unchanged since its creation in the 1690s.

p136 **Across**: 1 Coleus, 4 Theorem, 9 Novelette, 10 Riser, 11 Ends, 12 Navy, 13 Elle, 15 Totally, 17 Singer, 19 Teased, 21 Started, 24 Peel, 25 Omit, 26 Calf, 30 Odour, 31 Tarpaulin, 32 Dressed, 33 Pebble.

Down: 1 Contest, 2 Livid, 3 Ugli, 4 Twelves, 5 Eire, 6 Resilient, 7 Mersey, 8 Stingy, 14 Alas, 16 Therefore, 18 Noah, 20 Demoted, 21 Saturn, 22 Defence, 23 Uphold, 27 Ad lib, 28 Iris, 29 Safe.

HELIOTROPE – a plant that's popular not only for its flowers, ranging from mauve to blue, but also for its honey-like fragrance – often compared to the scent of baby powder!

p138 **Across**: 1 Borage, 4 Brigand, 9 Barrister, 10 Cocks, 11 Sort, 12 Acid, 13 Free, 15 Tussock, 17 Hangar, 19 Vandal, 21 Polenta, 24 Acts, 25 Bout, 26 Acer, 30 Unite, 31 Intention, 32 Legatee, 33 Couple.

Down: 1 Babysit, 2 Rarer, 3 Grip, 4 Burnish, 5 Inch, 6 Ascertain, 7 Duster, 8 Attack, 14 Ford, 16 Startling, 18 Null, 20 Leonine, 21 Petite, 22 Arrange, 23 Casual, 27 Chimp, 28 Tent, 29 Undo.

GRAN'S FAVOURITE – a clove-scented dianthus which has white flowers with dark pink-mauve centres and edges.

p140 **Across**: 1 Breeches, 5 Adults, 9 Ensue, 10 Conundrum, 12 Towns, 13 Ruts, 14 Fair, 16 Despot, 18 Example, 21 Prelude, 23 Hebrew, 25 East, 27 Brag, 28 Staff, 30 Vertebrae, 31 Opera, 32 Lights, 33 Defeated.

Down: 1 Breath, 2 Elsewhere, 3 Chess, 4 Excerpt, 6 Dine, 7 Larva, 8 Somerset, 11 Nitre, 15 Garb, 17 Plus, 19 Prevalent, 20 Upheaval, 22 Error, 23 Hygiene, 24 Afraid, 26 Sprig, 28 Shone, 29 Peat.

BUXUS SEMPERVIRENS – box – a compact slow-growing shrub which keeps its shape without having to be trimmed too frequently – useful for edging or for low hedges.

p142 **Across**: 1 Deutzia, 5 Drowsy, 9 Align, 10 Patchouli, 11 Pied, 12 Sere, 13 Robot, 15 Nectar, 17 Berberis, 20 Camellia, 21 Pardon, 23 Relic, 25 Tack, 27 Etna, 29 Utterance, 30 Agora, 31 Adrift, 32 Mahonia.

Down: 1 Deadpan, 2 Unite, 3 Zen, 4 Apple, 5 Dithered, 6 Other, 7 Slumbered, 8 Cistus, 14 Yawl, 16 Completed, 18 Brag, 19 Distinct, 20 Cornus, 22 Niagara, 24 Corgi, 26 Cream, 28 Thorn, 30 Ash.

p144 Across: 1 Esteemed, 5 Acacia, 9 Chair, 10 Show round, 12 Essay, 13 Raft, 14 Beer, 16 Rooted, 18 Riposte, 21 Admiral, 23 Warned, 25 Arts, 27 Pale, 28 Moral, 30 Charlotte, 31 Feign, 32 Azalea, 33 Adriatic.

Down: 1 Exceed, 2 Transform, 3 Early, 4 Ensured, 6 Card, 7 Chute, 8 Alderney, 11 Offer, 15 Spur, 17 Tare, 19 Spearmint, 20 La Mancha, 22 Least, 23 Weekend, 24 Clinic, 26 Tiara, 28 Mufti, 29 Glue.

MONEY MAKER – one of the most popular varieties of tomato.

p146 Across: 1 Meagre, 4 Compel, 10 Semicolon, 11 Earls, 12 Cane, 13 Software, 16 Sushi, 17 Tagetes, 19 New, 20 Mocking, 22 Lobes, 24 Plantain, 27 Pram, 31 Irate, 32 Unheard-of, 33 Canada, 34 Cosmea.

Down: 1 Music, 2 Almonds, 3 Rock, 5 Omega, 6 Perfect, 7 Lost, 8 Allowing, 9 Knot, 14 Hi-fi, 15 Isis, 16 Some, 17 Twilight, 18 Gull, 21 Captain, 23 Boredom, 25 Amend, 26 Trug, 28 Mafia, 29 Zinc, 30 Taco.

GEOFF HAMILTON – very popular gardening expert, broadcaster and writer. His gardens at Barnsdale are open to the public.

p148 Across: 1 Bergamot, 5 Calico, 9 Local, 10 Therefore, 12 Eclat, 13 Idea, 14 Isle, 16 Before, 18 Deepest, 21 Authors, 23 Prompt, 25 Quid, 27 Logo, 28 Close, 30 Insolence, 31 Robot, 32 Heehaw, 33 Obdurate.

Down: 1 Belief, 2 Recollect, 3 Allot, 4 Outside, 6 Abel, 7 Irons, 8 Omelette, 11 Emend, 15 Nero, 17 Oboe, 19 Euphorbia, 20 Vanquish, 22 Shown, 23 Proverb, 24 Kettle, 26 Issue, 28 Corfu, 29 Ella.

GOLDEN ROD – or Solidago, has narrow leaves and tiny yellow flowers in feathery plumes.

p150 Across: 1 Indigo, 4 Chaplet, 9 Indignant, 10 Tommy, 11 Tree, 12 Wide, 13 Eton, 15 Cycling, 17 Loiter, 19 Brazen, 21 Honesty, 24 Nude, 25 Bung, 26 Rove, 30 Relic, 31 Roundhead, 32 Wastrel, 33 Inland.

Down: 1 Idiotic, 2 Dodge, 3 Gags, 4 Citadel, 5 Ante, 6 Limitless, 7 Trying, 8 Earwig, 14 Ritz, 16 Corydalis, 18 Inns, 20 Neutral, 21 High-up, 22 Yielded, 23 Andrew, 27 Omega, 28 Scar, 29 Odin.

HIDCOTE – one of England's great gardens, Hidcote was designed and created by the horticulturist Major Lawrence Johnston. It is arranged as a series of outdoor 'rooms', each with a different character.

p152 Across: 1 Leeks, 4 Doubt, 7 Map, 9 Nicotiana, 10 Macaw, 11 Each, 13 Solidago, 17 Seaweed, 18 Mourned, 20 Goggles, 22 Precede, 23 Tarragon, 24 Beta, 28 Tokyo, 30 Great Dane, 32 Hay, 33 Shrub, 34 Needs.

Down: 1 Lance, 2 Etc, 3 Site, 4 Diamond, 5 Uranium, 6 Tom, 7 Macho, 8 Pawn, 12 Craig, 14 Amused, 15 Cellar, 16 Idle, 17 Sage, 19 Niece, 21 Swagger, 22 Proverb, 23 Tokay, 25 Areas, 26 Utah, 27 Stun, 29 Ops, 31 Ale.

KING EDWARD – one of the most popular potato varieties.

p154 **Across:** 1 Middle, 4 Treaty, 10 Calabrese, 11 Tarry, 12 Ants, 13 Arboreta, 16 Sidle, 17 Scarlet, 19 Via, 20 Laramie, 22 Helix, 24 Stressed, 27 Ha-ha, 31 Ruing, 32 Marauding, 33 Eighty, 34 Meagre.

Down: 1 Mocha, 2 Deleted, 3 Labs, 5 Retie, 6 Air mail, 7 Yo-yo, 8 Retrieve, 9 Zero, 14 Ream, 15 Styx, 16 Sole, 17 Sancerre, 18 Ache, 21 Resting, 23 Leading, 25 Right, 26 Semi, 28 Angle, 29 True, 30 Mute.

MESEMBRYANTHEMUM – popularly known as Livingstone daisy or ice plant – is extremely easy to grow and provides dazzling colours through summer and autumn.

p156 **Across:** 1 Cycle, 4 Mariner, 9 Mesmerism, 10 Brief, 11 Orbit, 13 Gold, 14 Myna, 16 Trained, 18 Sporran, 20 Gondola, 22 Cabaret, 24 Read, 26 Syon, 27 Syria, 28 Audio, 30 Marrowfat, 32 Dutiful, 33 Newer.

Down: 1 Comfort, 2 Cos, 3 Elect, 4 Mimulus, 5 Rib, 6 Noisy, 7 Refrain, 8 Singed, 12 Brawn, 15 Boob, 17 Nook, 19 Rarer, 20 Garland, 21 Abysmal, 22 Canary, 23 Tractor, 25 Audit, 27 Shown, 29 Oaf, 31 Few.

MRS BRADSHAW – a geum that produces lovely scarlet semi-double flowers shaped like small roses. It has a long blooming season – from May to July.

p158 **Across:** 1 Tapes, 4 Eddy, 6 Cats, 10 Ringlet, 11 West Ham, 12 Fur, 13 Holst, 14 Arson, 15 Cockatoo, 18 Begin, 20 Dosed, 21 Resolute, 23 Brace, 25 Elver, 28 Emu, 29 Torpedo, 30 Niblick, 31 Seek, 32 Adam, 33 Light.

Down: 1 Thrift, 2 Penurious, 3 Sylph, 4 Extol, 5 down tools, 7 Aphis, 8 Simenon, 9 Istanbul, 16 Kedgeree, 17 Threefold, 19 Gathering, 20 Debates, 22 Junket, 24 Agree, 26 Venom, 27 Rebel.

WISTERIA – not only one of the most beautiful climbing plants with its flowers of lilac, mauve, blue or white, but also a very easy plant to grow.

p160 **Across:** 1 Mecca, 4 Rhizome, 9 Donations, 10 Louts, 11 Laud, 12 Peas, 13 Omen, 16 Circa, 17 Aubrietia, 20 Prominent, 22 Cache, 24 Stay, 26 Drey, 27 Plea, 31 Reign, 32 Startling, 33 Blessed, 34 Mason.

Down: 1 Model, 2 Conquer, 3 Anti, 4 Rises, 5 Igloo, 6 Opulent, 7 Else, 8 Tolerate, 14 Sari, 15 Late, 16 Copy, 18 By the way, 19 Itch, 21 Outside, 23 Celsius, 25 Yanks, 26 Dosed, 28 Argon, 29 Grab, 30 Item.

MOSS CURLED – a very popular variety of parsley, with tightly curled rich green leaves.

p162 **Across:** 6 Jacob's Ladder, 10 Raise, 11 Inspector, 12 Croquet, 14 Astound, 16 Star of Bethlehem, 21 Theatre, 23 Impeded, 25 Optimists, 28 Dunes, 29 Solomon's Seal.

Down: 1 Casino, 2 Bole, 3 Pass, 4 Advent, 5 Brat, 7 Swift, 8 Crocus, 9 Arid, 13 UFO, 14 Art, 15 Ugh, 17 Awe, 18 Bee, 19 Lap, 20 Modest, 21 Thor, 22 Temple, 23 Ibsen, 24 Dental, 26 Toss, 27 Sumo, 28 Dose.

p164 **Across:** 1 Twinge, 4 Laramie, 9 Different, 10 Stale, 11 Yard, 12 Renowned, 15 Drosera, 16 Samurai, 18 Dot, 19 Absolve, 21 Article, 23 Altitude, 26 Snap, 30 Ripen, 31 Perpetual, 32 Palaces, 33 Larynx.

Down: 1 Toddy, 2 Inferno, 3 Glen, 4 Lotto, 5 Risen, 6 Meander, 7 Even, 8 Renegade, 13 Meal, 14 Mice, 15 Dual, 16 Standard, 17 Moth, 20 Scalpel, 22 Century, 24 Tonic, 25 Types, 27 Phlox, 28 Trap, 29 Hera.

WINTER ACONITE – Eranthis hyemalis – produces early yellow flowers between January and March.

p166 **Across:** 1 Twerp, 4 Bacchus, 9 Attorneys, 10 Undue, 11 Gazelle, 13 Osprey, 15 Ruby, 16 Lawn, 18 Tepid, 21 Shape, 22 Poet, 24 Play, 25 Gallon, 27 Cayenne, 31 Mango, 32 Checkmate, 34 Anemone, 35 Limit.

Down: 1 Twang, 2 Eft, 3 Peril, 4 Bassoon, 5 Crumpets, 6 Hedge, 7 Stew, 8 Nepeta, 12 Zebra, 14 Edgy, 15 Rash, 17 Woo, 19 Pylon, 20 Well-to-do, 22 Panache, 23 Exceed, 26 Annie, 28 Yokel, 29 Erect, 30 Emma, 33 Arm.

EARLY LAXTON – the earliest of all plums, producing fruit in early August.

p168 **Across:** 1 Squash, 4 Audible, 9 Recollect, 10 Chips, 11 Nave, 12 Merchant, 15 Halve, 16 Eastern, 18 Ell, 19 Merited, 21 Chary, 23 Blockage, 26 Kind, 30 Unfit, 31 In the main, 32 Reserve, 33 Esteem.

Down: 1 Siren, 2 Uncivil, 3 Solo, 4 Attic, 5 Dacca, 6 Brittle, 7 Ease, 8 Revealed, 13 Zest, 14 Only, 15 Hymn, 16 Elongate, 17 Sock, 20 Rebuffs, 22 Agitate, 24 Otter, 25 Knife, 27 Denim, 28 Burr, 29 Leis.

ALCHEMILLA MOLLIS – popularly known as lady's mantle – grown for both foliage and flowers, it will thrive in sun or shade.

p170 **Across:** 1 Cherub, 4 Capable, 9 Necessary, 10 Logic, 11 Squat, 12 Doncaster, 14 Article, 16 Elegant, 18 Carping, 20 Bittern, 22 Raspberry, 24 Laden, 25 Impel, 27 Adornment, 28 Forsake, 29 Shut up.

Down: 1 Canasta, 2 Encounter, 3 Upset, 4 Cayenne, 5 Pal, 6 Bigot, 7 Excerpt, 8 Candle, 13 Avert, 15 Climb, 17 Amendment, 18 Cardiff, 19 Garbage, 20 Blyton, 21 Nonstop, 23 Super, 24 Lunch, 26 Lea.

ACORN BANK – near Temple Sowerby in Cumbria, a delightful sheltered garden, noted for its herbs and its orchards growing old English fruit varieties.

p172 **Across:** 1 Slaps, 4 Miserable, 9 ABC, 10 Bar, 11 Eyesore, 12 Nosy, 13 Maxi, 14 Samba, 16 Horrible, 18 Dowse, 20 Nasty, 21 Insomnia, 22 Scows, 25 Stir, 27 Open, 30 Lesotho, 31 Coo, 32 Rye, 33 Disappear, 34 Noddy.

Down: 1 Swain, 2 Ancestors, 3 Subs, 4 Maria, 5 Specimens, 6 Reeds, 7 Bloom, 8 Elevate, 15 Bray, 17 Brimstone, 18 Damp, 19 Whispered, 20 Nestled, 23 Oasts, 24 Set up, 26 Incur, 28 Needy, 29 Soon.

PERCY THROWER – who died in 1988, was for three decades Britain's best-known and best-loved gardener, garden writer and broadcaster.

p174 **Across:** 1 Replica, 5 Reared, 8 Nylon, 9 Somerset, 11 Heap, 12 Pear, 13 Lower, 15 Ratio, 17 Spearmint, 20 Greyhound, 23 Risky, 25 Faith, 27 Rims, 28 Rhyl, 30 Cardigan, 31 Banal, 32 Corset, 33 Calming.

Down: 1 Rancher, 2 Polka, 3 Inn, 4 Answers, 5 Remorse, 6 April, 7 Edelweiss, 10 Trot, 14 Moth, 16 The Mikado, 18 Pan, 19 Rare, 20 Gift, 21 Upright, 22 Demonic, 24 Yule log, 26 Hides, 29 Hindi, 31 Bel.

ERNEST MARKHAM – a hardy red-flowered variety, flowering continuously and profusely through summer and autumn.

p176 **Across:** 1 Asses, 4 Western, 9 Brigadier, 10 Fling, 11 Raft, 12 Spry, 13 Show, 16 Calla, 17 Represent, 20 Annulment, 22 Relax, 24 Omar, 26 Wren, 27 Grow, 31 Own up, 32 Shipwreck, 33 Balance, 34 Rayon.

Down: 1 Amber, 2 Skilful, 3 Spam, 4 Worry, 5 Sofas, 6 Episode, 7 Nigh, 8 Disperse, 14 Pail, 15 Styx, 16 Cram, 18 Pathetic, 19 Earl, 21 Nominal, 23 Larceny, 25 Ripon, 26 Waste, 28 Waken, 29 Tomb, 30 Ewer.

WISLEY – between Cobham and Ripley in Surrey, is one of the four gardens of the Royal Horticultural Society. The others are Rosemoor in North Devon, Hyde Hall in Essex, and Harlow Carr in Yorkshire.

p178 **Across:** 1 Baffled, 5 Burrow, 8 Truck, 9 Charlotte, 11 Orgy, 12 Rome, 13 Roast, 15 Sisal, 17 Peculiar, 20 Bearable, 21 Ahead, 24 Sprog, 26 Team, 27 Ruta, 30 Chauffeur, 31 Amuse, 32 Detest, 33 Learned.

Down: 1 Buttons, 2 Flung, 3 Like, 4 Doctor, 5 Bracelet, 6 Ruler, 7 Ostracise, 10 Enter, 14 Ulna, 16 Staircase, 18 Utah, 19 Ill-treat, 20 Basic, 22 Dead end, 23 Barrel, 25 Gaffe, 28 U-turn, 29 Java.

EUONYMUS ALATUS – an attractive deciduous shrub which comes into its own in autumn when the leaves turn a brilliant red.

p180 **Across:** 1 Echinops, 5 Fiasco, 9 Mazes, 10 Stonecrop, 12 Tarry, 13 Over, 14 Spin, 16 Locust, 18 Sirloin, 21 Absolve, 23 Apathy, 25 Arch, 27 Esau, 28 Beryl, 30 Abandoned, 31 Cairo, 32 Talent, 33 Brussels.

Down: 1 Enmity, 2 Hazardous, 3 Nasty, 4 Pass out, 6 Ibex, 7 Strip, 8 Opponent, 11 Obeys, 15 Aria, 17 Ugly, 19 Otherwise, 20 Cataract, 22 Essen, 23 Asunder, 24 Elbows, 26 Crawl, 28 Backs, 29 Eden.

CAPABILITY BROWN – Lancelot Brown, the great 18th -century landscape gardener, acquired his nickname from telling his clients that their gardens had excellent "capabilities". He laid out the gardens at Blenheim, Kew, Stowe, and many others.

p182 **Across:** 1 Oast, 3 Chorus Girl, 10 Appal, 11 Robin Hood, 12 Guard, 13 Evil, 14 Isis, 16 Redcoat, 18 Humdrum, 21 Brewing, 23 Retinue, 24 Nett, 26 Rain, 27 Prawn, 30 Talking-to, 31 Owing, 32 Cherry Wine, 33 Vest.

Down: 1 Orange Robin, 2 Sepia, 4 Hardest, 5 Rubbish, 6 Sons, 7 Irons, 8 Led, 9 Gladioli, 15 Summer Night, 17 Die, 19 Metaphor, 20 Run, 22 Glasgow, 23 Rangoon, 25 Tulle, 28 Agile, 29 Tier, 30 Tic.

p184 **Across:** 1 Commute, 5 Thorns, 9 Rayon, 10 Seedlings, 11 Firm, 12 Meat, 13 Drake, 15 Leaves, 17 Leverets, 20 Immortal, 21 Whelks, 23 Handy, 25 Enid, 27 Step, 30 Lithuania, 31 Osaka, 32 Frugal, 33 Othello.

Down: 1 Careful, 2 Mayor, 3 Urns, 4 Ensue, 5 Treaties, 6 Oiled, 7 Nonpareil, 8 Assess, 14 Beer, 16 Axminster, 18 Echo, 19 Maternal, 20 Inhale, 22 Soprano, 24 Young, 26 Idaho, 28 Trail, 29 Loth.

MARGARET MERRIL – the flowers which are double, snowy white, urn-shaped and sweetly scented, are borne profusely throughout the summer and well into the autumn.

p186 **Across:** 1 Drip-dry, 5 Warmth, 9 Piece, 10 Elsewhere, 11 Oust, 12 Edge, 13 Nicer, 15 Actual, 17 Marriage, 20 Terminus, 21 Statue, 23 Realm, 25 Labs, 27 Uses, 30 Solicitor, 31 Rioja, 32 Inborn, 33 Liberty.

Down: 1 Diploma, 2 Ideas, 3 Duet, 4 Yield, 5 Wesleyan, 6 Rowan, 7 Trenchant, 8 Decree, 14 Maxi, 16 Tarpaulin, 18 Rota, 19 Bulletin, 20 Thrush, 22 Ecstasy, 24 Macho, 26 Beryl, 28 Scour, 29 Crab.

WINTER BEAUTY – a highly regarded dogwood not only for the beautiful tints of its autumn foliage but also the striking colours of its bare winter stems.

p188 **Across:** 1 Confess, 5 Crabby, 8 Humid, 9 Lengthen, 11 Buds, 12 Tame, 13 Range, 15 Trade, 17 Associate, 20 Hilarious, 23 Basic, 25 Gowns, 27 Used, 28 Move, 30 Obsolete, 31 Fraud, 32 Relent, 33 Younger.

Down: 1 Cohabit, 2 Nomad, 3 End, 4 Sultana, 5 Conkers, 6 After, 7 Biennials, 10 Bede, 14 Fear, 16 Allowable, 18 Sou, 19 Cubs, 20 High, 21 Opulent, 22 Scenery, 24 Cheddar, 26 Stoke, 29 Orang, 31 Flu.

SANTOLINA – popular for its silvery scented foliage.

p190 **Across**: 1 Thigh, 4 Lucifer, 9 Trenchant, 10 Title, 11 Data, 12 Ogre, 13 Huge, 16 Spade, 17 Resilient, 20 Injurious, 22 Reach, 24 Inks, 26 Whey, 27 Nine, 31 Guava, 32 Aristotle, 33 Day lily, 34 Mercy.

Down: 1 Toted, 2 Inertia, 3 Hock, 4 Let be, 5 Catch, 6 Fatigue, 7 Reed, 8 Kangaroo, 14 Pear, 15 Etch, 16 Slim, 18 Systemic, 19 Lira, 21 January, 23 Aviator, 25 Swami, 26 Weary, 28 Enemy, 29 Aged, 30 Stem.

GERTRUDE JEKYLL – in association with the architect Edward Lutyens, she designed more than 300 gardens for his buildings. These gardens and the books she wrote greatly influenced the use of colour planning in garden design.

p192 **Across**: 1 Wheedle, 5 Parma, 9 Noose, 10 Alligator, 11 Buys, 12 Veto, 13 Stoop, 15 Grenade, 18 Iterate, 20 Cheaper, 21 Denoted, 23 Might, 25 News, 27 Gods, 30 Innocuous, 31 Minor, 32 Yetis, 33 Stroppy.

Down: 1 Windbag, 2 Ebony, 3 Diet, 4 Erase, 5 Pilloried, 6 Regis, 7 Astronaut, 8 Triple, 14 Rasp, 16 Emergency, 17 Erroneous, 19 Erne, 20 Come in, 22 Destroy, 24 Tacit, 26 Wasps, 28 Own up, 29 Omar.

MASTERWORT – Astrantia major – a charming perennial with branched heads of neat pincushion flowers in summer. It will flourish in any conditions, but does best in moist soil.

p194 **Across**: 1 Opposed, 5 Beam, 9 Giddy, 10 Wiltshire, 11 Nil, 12 Acre, 13 Plaid, 15 Chamois, 17 Hatred, 20 Crooks, 21 Eminent, 24 Idaho, 26 Bake, 27 Had, 29 Ill at ease, 30 Ounce, 31 Scan, 32 Soloist.

Down: 1 Organic, 2 Pedal, 3 Skye, 4 downcast, 5 Bolder, 6 Aesop, 7 Disagree, 8 Needed, 14 Mock, 16 Adorable, 18 Akin, 19 Reckless, 20 Crisis, 22 Tidiest, 23 Obtain, 25 Optic, 27 Hindi, 28 Tool.

ENA HARKNESS – a hybrid tea with very fragrant bright crimson flowers, blooming all summer.

p196 **Across**: 1 Thrift, 4 Reaction, 10 Ample, 11 Expedited, 12 Twos, 13 Beholden, 16 Refuted, 17 Trapeze, 19 Magenta, 22 Babyish, 24 Disaster, 26 Seal, 30 Interfere, 31 Inert, 32 Weakness, 33 Plague.

Down: 1 Trait, 2 Reproof, 3 Flex, 5 Exploit, 6 Ceded, 7 Intense, 8 Nude, 9 Behead, 14 Stun, 15 Mesh, 16 Rime, 18 Alba, 20 Godetia, 21 Answers, 22 Brewer, 23 Iceberg, 25 Siren, 27 Lethe, 28 View, 29 Gill.

HELLEBORUS NIGER – the Christmas rose – so-called because it flowers around Christmas time. A good plant for a shady border.

223

p198 **Across**: 1 Mascara, 5 Thrush, 8 Large, 9 Colander, 11 Town, 12 Quay, 13 Elite, 15 Ashen,
17 Apologise, 20 Sentiment, 23 Dream, 25 Girls, 27 Runt, 28 Marc, 30 Angelica, 31 Flare,
32 Pepper, 33 Delilah.

Down: 1 Militia, 2 Straw, 3 Age, 4 Anchusa, 5 Tally-ho, 6 Range, 7 Sterilise, 10 Hebe,
14 Anti, 16 Hindrance, 18 Pun, 19 Odds, 20 Saga, 21 Earlier, 22 Tankard, 24 Macbeth,
26 Sweep, 29 Avail, 31 Fal.

*GAY SEARCH – gardening writer and broadcaster, best known as a presenter on the TV
programmes Front Gardens and Gardeners' World.*

p200 **Across**: 1 Giddy, 4 Snag, 6 Glow, 10 Algeria, 11 Sweater, 12 Cat, 13 Sued, 14 Depth,
16 Altitude, 19 Aesop, 21 Posed, 22 Las Vegas, 24 Tying, 26 Jump, 29 Bid, 31 Offence,
32 Despair, 33 Sane, 34 Coir, 35 Andes.

Down: 1 Glance, 2 Digitalis, 3 Yards, 4 Scare, 5 Also, 7 Lit up, 8 Worship, 9 Reed mace,
15 Less, 17 Indigent, 18 Ugly, 20 Starboard, 21 Pythons, 23 Adorns, 25 In fun, 27 Under,
28 Pasta, 30 Memo.

*GLOIRE DE DIJON – a favourite cottage garden rose, with beautiful scented buff-apricot
double flowers.*

p202 **Across**: 1 Allgold, 5 Hiccups, 9 Wealthier, 10 Enter, 11 Locum, 13 Erect, 14 Run,
15 Cornelia, 17 Hansa, 19 Virgo, 21 Delicata, 24 Rib, 26 Rubus, 28 Nadir, 29 Epsom,
30 Roosevelt, 32 Almonds, 33 Felicia.

Down: 1 As well, 2 Lea, 3 Ottoman, 4 Drive, 5 Horsetail, 6 Cheetah, 7 Utter, 8 Syringa,
12 Choir, 16 Ladybirds, 18 Noted, 19 Verbena, 20 Oarsmen, 22 Conceal, 23 Protea,
25 Besom, 27 Scoff, 31 Etc.